SAY GRACE:

A SCRIPTURAL FIELD GUIDE TO

WEIGHT LOSS

COMPILED BY
CLARICE G. JAMES

ENDORSEMENTS

In her first full-length nonfiction book, James serves as a conduit for what God says about food, the body, and the Spirit-filled life. The field guide shows careful research and scholarship, including drawing from six different Bible translations, and James addresses the reader in a cheerful, conversational style, while knowing when to step back and let the Scriptures speak for themselves. This is an excellent resource for anyone concerned about their weight or seeking a deeper walk with God. If you're a Christian, this will be the last "diet book" you ever buy.
—**Kathleen D. Bailey**, journalist and author of the Western Dreams historical romance series

I have had the privilege of knowing Clarice James for many years now. She is a truly gifted writer who has a serious passion for her craft. Her insights, ease of style, and delivery make reading her works a breath of fresh air. Beyond that, the genuineness of her faith and love for people make her works relevant and refreshing.
—**Rev. Dr. Paul R. Berube**, Senior Pastor, Gate City Church, Nashua, NH

This is an amazing resource that I can't wait to share with the Thin Within groups, classes, and my one-on-one clients. Clarice brings us straight to the Living Word—a veritable feast for our hungry hearts. To renew our minds, there is no finer resource than a collection of Scriptures

that fall into categories pertinent to what many of us are dealing with.
—**Heidi Bylsma-Epperson**, owner and coach at ThinWithin.org

This compilation of Scriptures is more than a handy guide for those of us who struggle to maintain healthy diets. It's a wellspring of godly wisdom for struggles of every sort, a spring that never runs dry. In *Say Grace* Clarice G. James gathers a band of angelic cheerleaders for us all. Bravo.
—**Linda Brooks Davis**, author Women of Rock Creek historical series

You need this book! Clarice has compiled the perfect collection of verses for the "thin within" to meditate and thrive upon in a world obsessed with fad diets, pills, and medical procedures. The diet industry is a lie, but Clarice shows us God's word is sharper than a two-edged sword. "Human beings understand and almost crave rules," she writes, but Paul tells us, "For we do not wrestle against flesh and blood, but against principalities, against powers, against the rulers of the darkness of this age (Eph 6:12)." This field guide is for everyone seeking God's love and acceptance. As Jesus states in Matt 11:29, "For I am gentle and humble." He beckons his children through his word laid out clearly by Clarice in *Say Grace*. You will want to digest every verse as I have to rely on Him, "... for God is not a god of confusion but of peace (1 Cor 14:35) and to live as God sees you.
—**Andy M. Davison, Psy.D.**, retired Navy Captain and author of *When Sunday Smiled*

Say Grace is a labor of love, a gift to you. Clarice James has compiled a treasure trove of Scripture designed to draw you into a deeper relationship with God and a deeper

appreciation of how you are "fearfully and wonderfully made." The Scriptures come alive, needing no commentary, and speak to your heart of God's love, care, and grace. As your reading continues and your journey deepens, you will find your health and perspective improving. Nourish your mind and your body with *Say Grace* and you will find your wonder of God's gift of grace is richer and more expansive than you ever imagined. I highly recommend this book and invite you to begin a journey to the heart of God—and a healthier you!
—**Dr. Cynthia Fantasia**, pastor, speaker, and author of *In the Lingering Light* (NavPress)

Say Grace: A Scriptural Field Guide to Weight Loss by Clarice James is an inspirational beacon for whatever life issues you're confronting, not just weight. It shares over a thousand Scriptures from six different Bible translations covering over two hundred alphabetical and indexed topics. And at the end of each topic, the reader is blessed with a short quip of the author's typical wit.
—**Janet Grunst**, author of *A Heart Set Free*, *A Heart for Freedom*, and *Setting Two Hearts Free*

What a wonderfully inspired resource Clarice has compiled to support all of us in our pursuit of healthy bodies and healthy lives. It's beautiful to have scriptural backup in a journey that can feel like a never-ending battle. "If God is for us, who can be against us"—even in the struggle at the plate and at the scales. Thank you for this well-researched and sorely needed book!
—**Lori Stanley Roeleveld**, author of *Running from a Crazy Man (and other adventures traveling with Jesus)*

Clarice James is the real deal. She loves God's Word, and God's Word has proven itself in her life. Whether or

not losing weight is your goal, *Say Grace: A Scriptural Field Guide to Weight Loss* is a valuable tool every Christian should keep close. You'll find its well-organized topical Scriptures, interspersed with James' signature wit and wisdom, applicable to every chapter of your holistic approach to life.
—**Terrie Todd**, faith and humor columnist and historical fiction author

Say Grace: A Scriptural Field Guide to Weight Loss
A compilation of over 1,000 Scripture passages covering 153-plus topics selected by Clarice G. James

COPYRIGHT NOTICE

Say Grace: A Scriptural Field Guide to Weight Loss

Cover and Interior Design: Derinda Babcock
Editor(s): Paul W. Conant, Deb Haggerty

PUBLISHED BY: Elk Lake Publishing, Inc., 35 Dogwood Drive, Plymouth, MA 02360, 2022

Library Cataloging Data

Names: James, Clarice G. (Clarice G. James)
Say Grace: A Scriptural Field Guide to Weight Loss / Clarice G. James

290 p. 23cm × 15cm (9in × 6 in.)

ISBN-13: 978-1-64949-694-2 (paperback) | 978-1-64949-695-9 (trade hardcover) | 978-1-64949-696-6 (trade paperback) | 978-1-64949-697-3 (e-book)

Key Words: Christian diet and weight loss; life application Scripture; emotional eating; overcoming food addiction; twelve-step program; breaking strongholds; freedom vs legalism

Library of Congress Control Number: 2022944382 Nonfiction

DEDICATION

To my "road manager" Debra Smith Bock: Bless you for traveling this journey with me. Without your thoughtful input, hands-on help, and keen sense of direction, I would have gotten lost—figuratively *and* literally. Your talent for taking me seriously while *simultaneously* shaking your head at my lack of practical knowledge is a rare skill, which helps keep me humble. For that, I thank you ... I think. [Smile.]

CONTENTS

FOREWORD

Today, many are experiencing uncertainty as to what is true in this polarized society we live in. We wonder where to turn for answers to the perplexing and painful situations in the world and in our own personal lives.

Perhaps you are struggling with burdensome extra pounds or more pressing issues, keeping you from experiencing God's amazing grace and the power of a surrendered life.

I'm honored to write this foreword for Clarice's book, *Say Grace: A Scriptural Field Guide to Weight Loss*, because she has effectively addressed a myriad of situations we confront in our day-to-day lives. She has provided poignant biblical truths that speak into those trials, temptations, and addictive behaviors which keep us from experiencing an obedient, liberated life!

No matter what phase of life you are in, focusing on Scripture, which is the same yesterday, today, and tomorrow, will renew your mind and free you from haunting fears of failure. It will lift your gaze and give you a heart filled with everlasting hope!

I'm reminded of Professor John Murray's words. "There is no circumstance or situation of life, in all its variety and detail for which the revelation of God's will, in inspired Scripture, is not a sufficient guide."[FN]

My prayer is that millions of believers and those seeking answers will read this insightful book and be set free to enjoy the abundant life we have been given in Christ Jesus!

"Then you will know the truth, and the truth will set you free" (John 8:32 NIV).

—**Judy Wardell Halliday** RN, founder of Thin Within Ministries, author, *Thin Within* and *Hunger Within*

PART 1: OVERVIEW

Say Grace: A Scriptural Field Guide to Weight Loss is NOT a diet but a compilation of over a thousand Scripture passages, covering 153-plus topics, intended to help you understand *and* overcome the reasons you turn to food before *or* instead of to God.

Say Grace is designed to be used daily as a simple and valuable tool during your weight-loss journey. Though you can simply read the guide from cover to cover, my goal with *Say Grace* is to give you a convenient and comprehensive guide to Scripture passages, which you can *apply* at the moment difficulties, questions, temptations, or tests and trials arise. As you pray, I believe the Lord will reveal just the right verses for you at just the right time. (The blank lines between the topics are for your notes or additional verses the Lord gives you.)

The decision to compile the passages in *Say Grace* without adding any personal comment (other than the Tidbits and Morsels between topics) was based on these three factors:

- I did not want my opinion to detract from God's Word.
- I did not want to influence any personal message God may have for you.

- I wanted you to examine your personal relationship with God versus your relationship with food, not in *my* voice, but in the voice of the Holy Spirit.

The Lord confirmed my decision in Jesus's words in John's gospel:

> [Jesus] My message is not my own; it comes from God who sent me. Anyone who wants to do the will of God will know whether my teaching is from God or is merely my own. Those who speak for themselves want glory only for themselves, but a person who seeks to honor the one who sent him speaks truth, not lies. (John 7:16–18 NLT)

Why *Say Grace*?

The title, like the prayer we say before meals, is a daily reminder of the abundant grace God has for us. Legalistic diets cannot make us righteous—even if we succeed at them for a time. God's grace is more powerful than any sin or habit. Through God's grace alone, we're able to break the stronghold of compulsive overeating (and other habitual sins).

> For the grace of God has appeared, bringing salvation for all people, training us to renounce ungodliness and worldly passions, and to live self-controlled, upright, and godly lives in the present age. (Titus 2:11–12 ESV)

The Seed Sprouted

I learned about this "grace-oriented approach to lasting weight loss" in Judy and Arthur Halliday's book *Thin Within* (Thomas Nelson 2002). I highly recommend you order a copy to fully understand the concept. Here is an excerpt from *Thin Within: Rebuilding God's Temple Workbook Series* (© 2003 Thin Within):

> Thin Within is a non-diet, grace-controlled approach to weight, food, and eating issues. It involves no calorie or fat-gram counting, nor weighing or measuring food. Thin Within teaches how to choose wisely when eating a variety of foods in response to the natural God-given signals of hunger and satisfaction. As a result, participants eat less food, make beneficial food choices, and naturally melt down to the size God intended. Success is not in following food rules, but rather in experiencing the transforming power of God's grace which empowers individuals to live the abundant life in Christ.
>
> We believe the focus must be on the Bible and the power of the Holy Spirit rather than on self-effort in order for lasting change to take place.
>
> At Thin Within we know with God's strength, biblical insights, and discerning choices, we can overcome temptation and effectively deal with everyday frustrations. God provides permanent solutions rather than quick fixes. When we approach weight loss, food, eating, and body-image issues from God's perspective and the power of the Holy Spirit, we are transformed from within, so we do not continue to go from one addiction to another.

Hearing from God

As I set out on this journey to glorify God in my eating, the Holy Spirit "highlighted" specific Scripture verses. The first passage was in 2 Timothy:

> All Scripture is breathed out by God and profitable for teaching, for reproof, for correction, and for training in righteousness, that the man of God may be complete, equipped for *every* good work. (2 Tim. 3:16–17 ESV) [Italics mine.]

"Even when it comes to weight loss?" I asked God.

"'In every good work,'" I *heard* him say.

Next, my search led me to Matthew's gospel:

> So do not worry, saying, "What shall we eat?" or "What shall we drink?" or "What shall we wear?" For the pagans run after all these things, and your heavenly Father knows that you need them. *But seek first his kingdom and his righteousness, and all these things will be given to you as well.*" (Matt. 6:31–33 NIV) [Italics mine.]

More and more, I sought God and his kingdom. The next passage the Holy Spirit revealed was from Colossians. My eyes sprang open, especially when I read the last sentence:

> Since you died with Christ to the elemental spiritual forces of this world, why, as though you still belonged to the world, do you submit to its rules: "Do not handle! Do not taste! Do not touch!"? These rules, which have to do with things that are all destined to perish with use, are based on merely human commands and teachings. *Such regulations indeed have an appearance of wisdom, with their self-imposed worship, their false humility and their harsh treatment of the body, but they lack any value in restraining sensual indulgence.* (Col. 2:20–23 NIV) [Italics mine.]

"Wow. Lord, are you saying I don't have to submit to fad diets, legalistic rules, or eat tasteless foods?"

"Yes, that is what I am saying," he said.

These verses in Mark's gospel confirmed his answer:

> [Jesus] "Are you so dull?" he asked. "Don't you see that nothing that enters a person from the outside can defile them? For it doesn't go into their heart but into their stomach, and then out of the body." *(In saying this, Jesus declared all foods clean.)* (Mark 7:18–19 NIV) [Italics mine.]

The more I read the Word, the more I hungered for God. This verse in Jeremiah excited me:

> Your words are what sustain me; they are food to my hungry soul. They bring joy to my sorrowing heart and delight me. How proud I am to bear your name, O Lord. (Jer. 15:16 TLB)

As you feed on God's Word daily, apply it to your behavior and choices. By his grace—not by your strength—the Holy Spirit will change you from the inside out one day at a time.

Once I diligently searched the Scriptures and applied them to my eating, I found God's abundant grace and freedom. As a result (and a bonus!) I lost my extra weight.

> Taste and see that the LORD is good; blessed is the one who takes refuge in him. (Ps. 34:8 NIV)

DIET EXPERTS & THEIR FOOD PLANS

My purpose with this field guide is to bring God and his Word to the forefront. Feeding on the Word is the best "diet" there is because God's Word nourishes and transforms you spiritually, emotionally, and physically!

I would like to believe the majority of those who craft diet plans and write diet books (Christians and non-Christians) start out with good intentions. Of course, as in any industry, you'll find others who are less scrupulous or "just in it for the money." I don't intend to point fingers or try to figure out which is which or who is who for you.

I am not a doctor, dietician, or nutritionist, so I will not tell you what types of foods to eat. I do not address the advantages or disadvantages of additive-free or "clean" food, gluten-free, keto, low-carb/no-carb, non-dairy, paleo, sugar-free, vegan, or vegetarian diets. All that talk wearies me.

Whether your conscience dictates you stay away from certain foods for moral or religious reasons, or your body responds better to others, is a decision made between you, your medical professionals, and God. Same goes for your ideal weight. [I always say my ideal weight is somewhere between, "Terrific! You're losing weight!" and "Have you been sick?"]

Under the Holy Spirit's guidance, you are free to eat whatever choice foods the Lord provides, as long as you don't make your type of food your god. For example, if the words "keto," "carbs," or "gluten" come to mind more often than the name of Jesus on any given day, you might want to reexamine or readjust your priorities.

Health & Medical Message

Possible dietary limitations or restrictions: If you have a diagnosed allergy, the potential for a negative and/or harmful drug/food interaction, or a medical condition (such as heart disease or type 2 diabetes), your diet will be limited.

Diet and quick weight-loss medications: If you are dependent on prescription and/or over-the-counter weight-loss medications, pray about giving them up so you can focus on applying God's Word to your eating habits. If your dependence has escalated to addiction, you may need to seek professional help as you wean yourself off the pharmaceuticals.

Diet supplements: If you are concerned the food available today isn't providing you with enough of the seven nutrients (carbohydrates, proteins, fats, vitamins, minerals, fiber, and water) essential to life and health, consider taking supplements. Your body, created by God, will tell you what you need if you pay attention.

Weight-loss surgery: If you've had weight-loss surgery (gastric bypass, sleeve gastrectomy, duodenal switch, or revision surgery for adjustable gastric band), it's time to turn your attention to applying God's Word to this hunger-satisfied way of eating. If you are considering weight-loss surgery to solve your weight problem, please pray about holding off until you have your eating under control.

Physical exercise: Keep moving! According to the Mayo Clinic, there are seven benefits of regular physical exercise:

- Boosts energy.
- Can be fun and social.
- Combats health conditions and diseases.
- Controls weight.
- Improves mood.
- Improves your sex life.
- Promotes better sleep.

Trauma: If you believe past or current trauma (such as sexual, physical, or verbal abuse or other emotional trauma) is contributing to your weight gain and/or eating disorder, I strongly recommend you seek professional counseling.

Biblical Application

For clarification and application, I used six different translations and/or paraphrases in this topical collection. Since the ESV is the primary resource used in this compilation, all abbreviations follow the ESV's format.

- English Standard Version (ESV) © 2001 Crossway Bibles
- The Living Bible (TLB) © 1971 Tyndale House Foundation
- The Message (MSG) © 1993 Eugene H. Peterson
- New International Version (NIV) © 2011 Biblica, Inc.

- New King James Version (NKJV), © 1982 Thomas Nelson
- New Living Translation (NLT) © 1996 Tyndale House Foundation

When reading the Scripture passages in this guide, keep in mind the Bible was written in Hebrew, Aramaic, and Greek over a period of two thousand-plus years. The Old and New Testaments reflect the culture of the times and various regions.

You will glean the intended meaning of the passages more easily if you become familiar with the different literary styles (e.g., epistles, gospels, historical narrative, law, poetry, prophecy, and wisdom) and literary devices (e.g., allusion, anthropomorphism, hyperbole, idiom, metaphor, parable, paradox, simile, and symbolism).

Of course, the most reliable form of interpretation is the Holy Spirit's witness as you meditate on each verse.

Topical Bible Study Concerns

The concerns of topical Bible studies are valid and include:

- Taking Scripture passages out of context to support your topic.
- Stretching the meaning of the passage to better fit your topic.
- Unknowingly, yet wrongly, applying a passage.
- Propping up a broad but shallow understanding of the topic or the passage.
- Using a translation or paraphrase simply because it supports your topic.

While compiling this field guide, I made every effort to address each of these concerns. I was also blessed to have input from a team of mature believers grounded in the Word. If, however, you come across a verse or passage you believe I have incorrectly applied to a topic, please email me at cjames@claricejames.com.

Important Note: This guide is NOT meant to replace your daily Bible reading and devotions. The richness and holiness of God's Word can only be fully realized through the study and meditation of the complete and Holy Bible.

Who Will Benefit from this Field Guide?

- Bible study groups
- Celebrate Recovery members
- Individuals of all ages
- Thin Within members
- Twelve Step programs
- Other Christ-centered weight-loss groups

Not a Believer in Jesus Christ?

If you have not accepted Jesus Christ as your Savior and the Lord of your life, the truth is you may not "get" this new way of eating or understand how to apply the Scripture passages. To see how you can have a personal relationship with Jesus, go to Appendix II. His joy and peace await you!

Five Statements Worth Repeating

1. *Say Grace: A Scriptural Field Guide to Weight Loss* is NOT a diet but a compilation of over a thousand Scripture passages covering 153-plus topics, intended to help you understand *and* overcome the reasons you turn to food before *or* instead of to God.
2. Legalistic diets cannot make us righteous—even if we succeed at them for a time. God's grace is more powerful than any habit or sin. Through God's

grace alone, we're able to break the stronghold of compulsive overeating (and other habitual sins).

3. My purpose with this field guide is to bring God and his Word to the forefront. I believe feeding on the Word of God is the best "diet" there is because God's Word nourishes and transforms you spiritually, emotionally, *and* physically!
4. This guide is NOT meant to replace your daily Bible reading or devotions. The richness and holiness of God's Word can only be fully realized through the study and meditation of the complete and Holy Bible.
5. If you have not accepted Jesus Christ as your Savior and the Lord of your life, the truth is you may not "get" this new way of eating or understand how to apply the Scripture passages. To see how you can have a saving and personal relationship with Jesus, go to Appendix II. His joy and peace await you!

Five Foundational Scripture Verses

1. 2 Timothy 3:16–17 (ESV): All Scripture is breathed out by God and profitable for teaching, for reproof, for correction, and for training in righteousness, that the man of God may be complete, equipped for *every* good work. [Italics mine.]
2. Matthew 6:31–33 (NIV): [Jesus says] So do not worry, saying, "What shall we eat?" or "What shall we drink?" or "What shall we wear?" For the pagans run after all these things, and your heavenly Father knows that you need them. *But seek first his kingdom and his righteousness, and all these things will be given to you as well.* [Italics mine.]
3. Colossians 2:20–23 (NIV): Since you died with Christ to the elemental spiritual forces of this world, why, as though you still belonged to the world, do you

submit to its rules: "Do not handle! Do not taste! Do not touch!"? These rules, which have to do with things that are all destined to perish with use, are based on merely human commands and teachings. *Such regulations indeed have an appearance of wisdom, with their self-imposed worship, their false humility, and their harsh treatment of the body, but they lack any value in restraining sensual indulgence.* [Italics mine.]

4. Mark 7:18–19 (NIV): "Are you so dull?" he asked. "Don't you see that nothing that enters a person from the outside can defile them? For it doesn't go into their heart but into their stomach, and then out of the body." *(In saying this, Jesus declared all foods clean.)* [Italics mine.]
5. Jeremiah 15:16 (TLB): Your words are what sustain me; they are food to my hungry soul. They bring joy to my sorrowing heart and delight me. How proud I am to bear your name, O Lord.

PART II: KEY PRINCIPLES

Still Looking for "The Diet"?

Some of you are still flipping through these pages asking, "But where's the diet? Where are the rules? How do I know what to eat or how much?"

I get it. Human beings understand and almost crave rules—even when we're not successful at following them. Freedom, on the other hand, can be scary because it involves making choices, acting responsibly, being accountable, and depending on God, not on yourself, another person, or a weight-loss program.

Again, the theme of this field guide is more about *why* you overeat than *what* you eat.

Rather than a list of strict rules, I have included Scripture-based principles to guide you. Remember, you're not on your own; God's got you!

Five Key Spiritual Principles

1. Meditate on God's Word daily, applying Scripture to your behavior and eating. The more you feed on God's Word and speak it out loud, the less you will turn to food. Don't trust me on this; trust God.
2. Pray often in Jesus's name and talk to him. The closer your relationship with Jesus, the stronger your desire to obey him.

3. Confess and repent, then accept God's grace, which enables you not to sin, yet covers your imperfections, mistakes, and overindulgences.
4. Surrender! The battle belongs to the Lord. This is not replacement theology. You cannot replace overeating with anything else except the Lord, including exercise, fasting, counting calories or carbs, "being good," taking drugs, suctioning fat, and/or following legalistic rules or trendy diets.
5. Praise God! His Holy Spirit is changing you, moment by moment, from the inside out.

Five Key Emotional Principles

1. God gave you emotions for your good, to use as a guide or gauge, not as a weapon or an excuse to overindulge. There are no good reasons to purposely overeat; they are *excuses* you use to justify your behavior.
2. When you eat apart from hunger, you are usually turning to food out of an emotional need—a need only the Lord can fill. No amount of food will assuage your anger and bitterness, lessen your anxiety or grief, clarify your thinking, stop you from blaming others for your problems, or get you through a tough time quicker.
3. Don't put "comfort food" on the same level as God. Overeating never solves problems; it just creates more of them.
4. Physical exhaustion and lack of sleep amplify emotions and often sabotage good intentions and self-control.
5. Stay alert for those temptations and mood swings lurking around every corner. Examine them closely,

identify them for what they are, and ask for help right away.

Five Key Diet/Eating Principles

1. Your body is wonderfully and fearfully made by God. He has programmed it to alert you to your need for food and water. In this new mindful way of eating, you'll need to *listen* to what your body is calling for—vitamins, minerals, protein, fats, water, and/or carbohydrates.
2. Barring any medical conditions, doctor's orders, or personal convictions, you are free to eat any and all types of foods. God gave "choice foods" to his people, but it doesn't hurt to read labels as long as you don't turn label reading into a religion. Note: If, at first, some of your favorite foods trigger compulsive eating, stay away from those foods until you have overcome the temptation to overindulge.
3. Wait for true stomach hunger. (The Thin Within program refers to true stomach hunger as 0.) When you sit down to have a meal, eliminate distractions, and focus on tasting and enjoying God's provisions. Eat slowly and stop when you are satisfied—not stuffed. (Thin Within refers to satisfaction as 5.)
4. Restricted food plans or fad diets (no matter how diligent you are in following them)—will not bring you closer to God or result in attaining the freedom God has intended for you.
5. Remember, eat out of *hunger,* not by the clock, event, habit, holiday, or tradition. Don't worry. You will learn how to adjust your hunger so you can participate fully in times of celebration.

Five Key Relational Principles

1. God should be your number one confidant. Get away with him as often as possible.
2. Partner with one or two others for the sake of accountability. Reevaluate this relationship periodically and change partners and/or advisers as the Holy Spirit leads.
3. Diet promoters and miracle plan evangelists will not agree with your new "lawless" food plan. They are legalists who want you to follow their specific rules. When people ask about your "diet," be discriminating with whom you share. "For those [freedom fighters] who understand, no explanation is necessary. For those [legalists] who don't, no explanation will suffice."
4. Don't be too hard on others—or yourself.
5. Family, friends, fellow believers, and coworkers can and will impact your relationship with food—either negatively or positively. Stay alert!

Five Key Lifestyle Principles

1. As Jesus said in Matthew 22:37–39 (MSG), '"Love the Lord your God with all your passion and prayer and intelligence.' This is the most important, the first on any list. But there is a second to set alongside it: 'Love others as well as you love yourself.'"
2. Your lifestyle choices will impact your eating. Portion control can be tough at all-you-can-eat buffets. Be ready to say, "No, thank you" in a positive, non-defensive way. To accommodate and enjoy holiday traditions and other social occasions, you may need to adjust your eating prior to the event.

3. Participate in a healthy and appropriate form of exercise—not because it's required or forced on you, but because it's good for your body and health. Also, be careful not to use exercise as an excuse to overindulge.
4. Regularly evaluate your progress to avoid slipping back into bondage to food and/or legalistic eating. Just because you *can* eat anything, doesn't mean you should.
5. Revisit your goals and the reasons behind them. Do they glorify God? Or has this new way of eating become all about you?

Final Exhortation

In obedience and joy, feed on a daily diet of the Word of God. Taste it, digest it, be satisfied, and be nourished. Reading and applying the Word isn't an instant fix; transformation takes time, but change will come.

Isaiah 61:7 (NIV) describes the double reward you can expect: "Instead of your shame you will receive a double portion, and instead of disgrace you will rejoice in your inheritance. And so you will inherit a double portion in your land, and everlasting joy will be yours."

PART III: TOPICAL FIELD GUIDE

Part II contains Bible passages covering 153 topics, which relate specifically to your walk with God and your relationship with food.

Abide in God

[Jesus] I am the true vine, and My Father is the vinedresser. Every branch in Me that does not bear fruit He takes away; and every branch that bears fruit He prunes, that it may bear more fruit. You are already clean because of the word which I have spoken to you. Abide in Me, and I in you. As the branch cannot bear fruit of itself, unless it abides in the vine, neither can you, unless you abide in Me. I am the vine, you are the branches. He who abides in Me, and I in him, bears much fruit; for without Me you can do nothing. (John 15:1–5 NKJV)

As you therefore have received Christ Jesus the Lord, so walk in Him, rooted and built up in Him and established in the faith, as you have been taught, abounding in it with thanksgiving. (Col. 2:6–7 NKJV)

And now, children, stay with Christ. Live deeply in Christ. Then we'll be ready for him when he appears, ready to receive him with open arms, with no cause for red-faced guilt or lame excuses when he arrives. (1 John 2:28 MSG)

> No one who abides in him keeps on sinning; no one who keeps on sinning has either seen him or known him. (1 John 3:6 ESV)

> By this we know that we abide in him and he in us, because he has given us of his Spirit. (1 John 4:13 ESV)

Tidbits & Morsels: Don't try to figure everything out. God's already done that. You'll find the answers in his Word.

____

____

____

Acceptance & Admittance

> Then I let it all out; I said, "I'll come clean about my failures to God." Suddenly the pressure was gone—my guilt dissolved, my sin disappeared. (Ps. 32:5 MSG)

> A man who refuses to admit his mistakes can never be successful. But if he confesses and forsakes them, he gets another chance. (Prov. 28:13 TLB)

> If we claim that we're free of sin, we're only fooling ourselves. A claim like that is errant nonsense. On the other hand, if we admit our sins—simply come clean about them—he won't let us down; he'll be true to himself. He'll forgive our sins and purge us of all wrongdoing. If we claim that we've never sinned, we out-and-out contradict God—make a liar out of him. A claim like that only shows off our ignorance of God. (1 John 1:8–10 MSG)

Tidbits & Morsels: Your problem with food isn't someone else's fault. Once you accept that truth, admit it to a person you trust.

____

____

____

Accountability

[Jesus] A promise is a promise. What difference does it make if you make your promise inside or outside a house of worship? A promise is a promise. God is present, watching and holding you to account regardless. (Matt. 23:21–22 MSG)

[Jesus] And a servant who knows what the master wants, but isn't prepared and doesn't carry out those instructions, will be severely punished. But someone who does not know, and then does something wrong, will be punished only lightly. When someone has been given much, much will be required in return; and when someone has been entrusted with much, even more will be required. (Luke 12:47–48 NLT)

You have no right to criticize your brother or look down on him. Remember, each of us will stand personally before the Judgment Seat of God. For it is written, "As I live," says the Lord, "every knee shall bow to me and every tongue confess to God." Yes, each of us will give an account of himself to God. (Rom. 14:10–12 TLB)

Nothing in all creation is hidden from God's sight. Everything is uncovered and laid bare before the eyes of him to whom we must give account. (Heb. 4:13 NIV)

The people I love, I call to account—prod and correct and guide so that they'll live at their best. Up on your feet, then! About face! Run after God! (Rev. 3:19 MSG)

Tidbits & Morsels: Be accountable to people who will hold you accountable.

Advice & Counsel

The counsel of the LORD stands forever, the plans of His heart to all generations. (Ps. 33:11 NKJV)

Where there is no guidance, a people falls, but in an abundance of counselors there is safety. (Prov. 11:14 ESV)

Arrogant know-it-alls stir up discord, but wise men and women listen to each other's counsel. (Prov. 13:10 MSG)

Leave the presence of a fool, for there you do not meet words of knowledge. (Prov. 14:7 ESV)

It is better to be a poor but wise youth than to be an old and foolish king who refuses all advice. (Eccl. 4:13 TLB)

Words of the wise, spoken quietly, should be heard rather than the shout of a ruler of fools. (Eccl. 9:17 NKJV)

Follow the pattern of the sound words that you have heard from me [Paul], in the faith and love that are in Christ Jesus. (2 Tim. 1:13 ESV)

Tidbits & Morsels: Always weigh the advice of others against the Word of God.

ANGER & BITTERNESS

Bridle your anger, trash your wrath, cool your pipes—it only makes things worse. (Ps. 37:8 MSG)

Whoever is slow to anger has great understanding, but he who has a hasty temper exalts folly. (Prov. 14:29 ESV)

Don't ever say, "I'll get you for that!" Wait for God; he'll settle the score. (Prov. 20:22 MSG)

If you are angry, don't sin by nursing your grudge. Don't let the sun go down with you still angry—get over it quickly; for when you are angry, you give a mighty foothold to the devil. ... Stop being mean, bad-tempered, and angry. Quarreling, harsh words, and dislike of others should have no place in your lives. (Eph. 4:26–27, 31 TLB)

Therefore I [Paul] want the men everywhere to pray, lifting up holy hands without anger or disputing. (1 Tim. 2:8 NIV)

Refuse to get involved in inane discussions; they always end up in fights. God's servant must not be argumentative, but a gentle listener and a teacher who keeps cool, working firmly but patiently with those who refuse to obey. (2 Tim 2:23–24 MSG)

Look after each other so that none of you fails to receive the grace of God. Watch out that no poisonous root of bitterness grows up to trouble you, corrupting many. (Heb. 12:15 NLT)

Know this, my beloved brothers: let every person be quick to hear, slow to speak, slow to anger; for the anger of man does not produce the righteousness of God. (James 1:19–20 ESV)

Tidbits & Morsels: Don't binge on bitterness; surrender your anger to God.

____

____

____

Anxiety & Stress

Anxiety in the heart of man causes depression, but a good word makes it glad. (Prov. 12:25 NKJV)

[Jesus] The seed cast in the weeds represents the ones who hear the kingdom news but are overwhelmed with worries about all the things they have to do and all the things they want to get. The stress strangles what they heard, and nothing comes of it. (Mark 4:18–19 MSG)

[Jesus] If then God so clothes the grass, which today is in the field and tomorrow is thrown into the oven, how much more will He clothe you, O you of little faith? And do not seek what you should eat or what you should drink, nor have an anxious mind. For all these things the nations of the world seek after, and your Father knows that you need these things. But seek the kingdom of God, and all these things shall be added to you. Do not fear, little flock, for it is your Father's good pleasure to give you the kingdom. (Luke 12:28–32 NKJV)

The Lord is at hand; do not be anxious about anything, but in everything by prayer and supplication with thanksgiving let your requests be made known to God. And the peace of God, which surpasses all understanding, will guard your hearts and your minds in Christ Jesus. (Phil. 4:5–7 ESV)

So we can confidently say, "The Lord is my helper; I will not fear; what can man do to me?" (Heb. 13:6 ESV)

Cast all your anxiety on him because he cares for you. (1 Pet. 5:7 NIV)

Tidbits & Morsels: Find one example in the Bible where Jesus ate to relieve stress. Eating to relieve anxiety does not work. But you knew that already, didn't you?

____

____

____

Appetite

Some [the redeemed of the Lord] wandered in desert wastelands, finding no way to a city where they could settle. They were hungry and thirsty, and their lives ebbed away. Then they cried out to the Lord in their trouble, and he delivered them from their distress. He led them by a straight way to a city where they could settle. Let them give thanks to the Lord for his unfailing love and his wonderful deeds for mankind, for he satisfies the thirsty and fills the hungry with good things. (Ps. 107:4–9 NIV)

The Lord does not let the righteous go hungry, but he thwarts the craving of the wicked. (Prov. 10:3 NIV)

An appetite for good brings much satisfaction, but the belly of the wicked always wants more. (Prov. 13:25 MSG)

A worker's appetite works for him; his mouth urges him on. (Prov. 16:26 ESV)

When you sit down to eat with a ruler, consider carefully what is before you; and put a knife to your throat if you are a man given to appetite. Do not desire his delicacies, for they are deceptive food. (Prov. 23:1–3 NKJV)

All the labor of man is for his mouth, and yet the soul is not satisfied. (Eccl. 6:7 NKJV)

> When your words showed up, I ate them—swallowed them whole. What a feast! What delight I took in being yours, O God, God-of-the-Angel-Armies! (Jer. 15:16 MSG)

Tidbits & Morsels: Like your vehicle's fuel gauge, let your appetite tell you when you need a refill.

Apply God's Word

> I have stored up your word in my heart, that I might not sin against you. (Ps. 119:11 ESV)

> Your word is a lamp to my feet and a light to my path. (Ps. 119:105 NKJV)

> My child, pay attention to what I say. Listen carefully to my words. Don't lose sight of them. Let them penetrate deep into your heart, for they bring life to those who find them, and healing to their whole body. (Prov. 4:20–22 NLT)

> [Jesus] He replied, "Yes, but even more blessed are all who hear the Word of God and put it into practice." (Luke 11:28 TLB)

> The whole Bible was given to us by inspiration from God and is useful to teach us what is true and to make us realize what is wrong in our lives; it straightens us out and helps us do what is right. It is God's way of making us well prepared at every point, fully equipped to do good to everyone. (2 Tim. 3:16–17 TLB)

> For the word of God is living and powerful, and sharper than any two-edged sword, piercing even to the division of soul and spirit, and of joints and marrow, and is a

> discerner of the thoughts and intents of the heart. (Heb. 4:12 NKJV)
>
> But be doers of the word, and not hearers only, deceiving yourselves. For if anyone is a hearer of the word and not a doer, he is like a man observing his natural face in a mirror; for he observes himself, goes away, and immediately forgets what kind of man he was. But he who looks into the perfect law of liberty and continues in it, and is not a forgetful hearer but a doer of the work, this one will be blessed in what he does. (James 1:22–25 NKJV)

Tidbits & Morsels: Carry this field guide with you so you can feed on God's Word throughout the day. Don't take my word for it; take God's Word for it.

____

____

____

Assume or Project

> Listen for God's voice in everything you do, everywhere you go; he's the one who will keep you on track. Don't assume that you know it all. Run to God! Run from evil! (Prov. 3:6–7 MSG)
>
> A man's heart plans his way, but the Lord directs his steps. (Prov. 16:9 NKJV)
>
> To answer before listening—that is folly and shame. (Prov. 18:13 NLT)
>
> Don't jump to conclusions—there may be a perfectly good explanation for what you just saw. (Prov. 25:8 MSG)

> Don't brag about your plans for tomorrow—wait and see what happens. (Prov. 27:1 TLB)

> Come now, you who say, "Today or tomorrow we will go into such and such a town and spend a year there and trade and make a profit"— yet you do not know what tomorrow will bring. What is your life? For you are a mist that appears for a little time and then vanishes. Instead you ought to say, "If the Lord wills, we will live and do this or that." As it is, you boast in your arrogance. All such boasting is evil. (James 4:13–16 ESV)

Tidbits & Morsels: Ask, don't assume; plan, don't project.

____

____

____

Avoidance vs. Confrontation

> Don't secretly hate your neighbor. If you have something against him, get it out into the open; otherwise you are an accomplice in his guilt. (Lev. 19:17 MSG)

> Confront me [Job] with the truth and I'll shut up, show me where I've gone off the track. Honest words never hurt anyone, but what's the point of all this pious bluster? (Job 6:24–25 MSG)

> Know-it-alls don't like being told what to do; they avoid the company of wise men and women. (Prov. 15:12 MSG)

> Better is open rebuke than hidden love. (Prov. 27:5 ESV)

> In the end, people appreciate honest criticism far more than flattery. (Prov. 28:23 NLT)

> [Jesus] If a brother sins against you, go to him privately and confront him with his fault. If he listens and

confesses it, you have won back a brother. (Matt. 18:15 TLB)

You're not getting by with anything. Every refusal and avoidance of God adds fuel to the fire. (Rom. 2:5 MSG)

Therefore, putting away lying, "Let each one of you speak truth with his neighbor," for we are members of one another.(Eph. 4:25 NKJV)

Tidbits & Morsels: Both avoidance and confrontation can be painful; but consider this: avoidance lasts longer.

____

____

____

Backslide or Relapse

Unless the LORD had given me help, I would soon have dwelt in the silence of death. When I said, "My foot is slipping," your unfailing love, LORD, supported me. When anxiety was great within me, your consolation brought me joy. (Ps. 94:17–19 NIV)

Though our iniquities testify against us, act, O LORD, for your name's sake; for our backslidings are many; we have sinned against you. (Jer. 14:7 ESV)

[Jesus] When a defiling evil spirit is expelled from someone, it drifts along through the desert looking for an oasis, some unsuspecting soul it can bedevil. When it doesn't find anyone, it says, 'I'll go back to my old haunt.' On return it finds the person spotlessly clean, but vacant. It then runs out and rounds up seven other spirits more evil than itself and they all move in, whooping it up. That person ends up far worse off than if he'd never gotten cleaned up in the first place. (Matt. 12:43–45 MSG)

For we all stumble in many ways. And if anyone does not stumble in what he says, he is a perfect man, able also to bridle his whole body. (James 3:2 ESV)

Obey God because you are his children; don't slip back into your old ways—doing evil because you knew no better. (1 Pet. 1:14 TLB)

Watch out that you do not lose what we have worked so hard to achieve. Be diligent so that you receive your full reward. (2 John 8 NLT)

Tidbits & Morsels: Think long term, especially if you've had a couple of bad days. With God's help, you can do this!

Bad Habits & Useless Traditions

But if you do not drive out the inhabitants of the land from before you, then it shall be that those whom you let remain shall be irritants in your eyes and thorns in your sides, and they shall harass you in the land where you dwell. (Num. 33:55 NKJV)

[Jesus]: (The Pharisees and all the Jews do not eat unless they give their hands a ceremonial washing, holding to the tradition of the elders. When they come from the marketplace they do not eat unless they wash. And they observe many other traditions, such as the washing of cups, pitchers and kettles.) So the Pharisees and teachers of the law asked Jesus, "Why don't your disciples live according to the tradition of the elders instead of eating their food with defiled hands?" He replied, "Isaiah was right when he prophesied about you hypocrites; as it is written: 'These people honor me with their lips, but their hearts are far from me. They

> worship me in vain; their teachings are merely human rules.' You have let go of the commands of God and are holding on to human traditions." And he continued, "You have a fine way of setting aside the commands of God in order to observe your own traditions!" (Mark 7:3–9 NIV)

> Don't copy the behavior and customs of this world but be a new and different person with a fresh newness in all you do and think. Then you will learn from your own experience how his ways will really satisfy you. (Rom. 12:2 TLB)

> See to it that no one takes you captive by philosophy and empty deceit, according to human tradition, according to the elemental spirits of the world, and not according to Christ. (Col. 2:8 ESV)

> So you must live as God's obedient children. Don't slip back into your old ways of living to satisfy your own desires. You didn't know any better then. (1 Pet. 1:14 NLT)

Tidbits & Morsels: Don't eat by the clock or out of habit. Wait for hunger to arrive; it's never late. Remember, bad eating habits don't happen overnight. Neither do good ones. It takes practice, patience, and time.

____

____

____

Balance & Moderation

> Moderation is better than muscle, self-control better than political power. (Prov. 16:32 MSG)

> Hear, my son, and be wise, and direct your heart in the way. Be not among drunkards or among gluttonous eaters of meat, for the drunkard and the glutton will come to poverty, and slumber will clothe them with rags. (Prov. 23:19–21 ESV)

> Where there is no revelation, the people cast off restraint; but happy is he who keeps the law. (Prov. 29:18 NKJV)

> [Jesus] When you're celebrating a wedding, you don't skimp on the cake and wine. You feast. Later you may need to exercise moderation, but this isn't the time. As long as the bride and groom are with you, you have a good time. When the groom is gone, the fasting can begin. No one throws cold water on a friendly bonfire. This is Kingdom Come! (Luke 5:34–35 MSG)

> All things are lawful for me, but all things are not helpful. All things are lawful for me, but I will not be brought under the power of any. (1 Cor. 6:12 NKJV)

Tidbits & Morsels: Change up your menu by adding some color—green, for instance. Avoid an overabundance of any one type of food—especially sugar, salt, carbs, and caffeine.

Battle & Fight

> When you prepare for battle, the priest must come forward to speak to the troops. He will say to them, "Listen to me, all you men of Israel! Do not be afraid as you go out to fight your enemies today! Do not lose heart or panic or tremble before them. For the Lord your God is going with you! He will fight for you against

> your enemies, and he will give you victory!" (Deut. 20:2–4 NLT)
>
> Thus says the LORD to you: "Do not be afraid nor dismayed because of this great multitude, for the battle is not yours, but God's." (2 Chron. 20:15 NKJV)
>
> Contend, LORD, with those who contend with me; fight against those who fight against me. (Ps. 35:1 NIV)
>
> Give us help from trouble, for the help of man is useless. Through God we will do valiantly, for it is He who shall tread down our enemies. (Ps. 108:12-13 NKJV)
>
> Finally, my brethren, be strong in the Lord and in the power of His might. Put on the whole armor of God, that you may be able to stand against the wiles of the devil. For we do not wrestle against flesh and blood, but against principalities, against powers, against the rulers of the darkness of this age, against spiritual hosts of wickedness in the heavenly places. Therefore take up the whole armor of God, that you may be able to withstand in the evil day, and having done all, to stand. Stand therefore, having girded your waist with truth, having put on the breastplate of righteousness, and having shod your feet with the preparation of the gospel of peace; above all, taking the shield of faith with which you will be able to quench all the fiery darts of the wicked one. And take the helmet of salvation, and the sword of the Spirit, which is the word of God; praying always with all prayer and supplication in the Spirit, being watchful to this end with all perseverance and supplication for all the saints—(Eph. 6:10–18 NKJV)

Tidbits & Morsels: Eyes forward—now march! The battle belongs to the Lord!

____

____

____

Be Still & Listen

> The Lord said, "Go out and stand on the mountain in the presence of the Lord, for the Lord is about to pass by." Then a great and powerful wind tore the mountains apart and shattered the rocks before the Lord, but the Lord was not in the wind. After the wind there was an earthquake, but the Lord was not in the earthquake. After the earthquake came a fire, but the Lord was not in the fire. And after the fire came a gentle whisper. When Elijah heard it, he pulled his cloak over his face and went out and stood at the mouth of the cave. (1 Kings 19:11–13 NIV)

> Rest in the Lord, and wait patiently for Him; do not fret because of him who prospers in his way, because of the man who brings wicked schemes to pass. Cease from anger, and forsake wrath; do not fret—it only causes harm. (Ps. 37:7–8 NKJV)

> He says, "Be still and know that I am God." (Ps. 46:10 NIV)

> Lord, I am not proud and haughty. I don't think myself better than others. I don't pretend to "know it all." I am quiet now before the Lord, just as a child who is weaned from the breast. Yes, my begging has been stilled. (Ps. 131:1–2 TLB)

> God, the Master, The Holy of Israel, has this solemn counsel: "Your salvation requires you to turn back to me and stop your silly efforts to save yourselves. Your strength will come from settling down in complete dependence on me—the very thing you've been unwilling to do." (Isa. 30:15 MSG)

Tidbits & Morsels: If you lean in and listen quietly, the Holy Spirit will reveal God's unique plan for your life—a full life beyond food!

Be Strong & Courageous

Have I not commanded you? Be strong and courageous. Do not be frightened, and do not be dismayed, for the Lord your God is with you wherever you go. (Josh. 1:9 ESV)

David strengthened himself with trust in his God. (1 Sam. 30:6 MSG)

So be strong and courageous, all you who put your hope in the Lord! (Ps. 31:24 NLT)

If you falter in a time of trouble, how small is your strength! (Prov. 24:10 NIV)

Strengthen the weak hands, and make firm the feeble knees. Say to those who are fearful-hearted, "Be strong, do not fear! Behold, your God will come with vengeance, with the recompense of God; He will come and save you." (Isa. 35:3–4 NKJV)

I eagerly expect and hope that I will in no way be ashamed but will have sufficient courage so that now as always Christ will be exalted in my body, whether by life or by death. (Phil. 1:20 NIV)

Tidbits & Morsels: Do you really think God expects you to be strong and courageous without his help? Step out in faith! He will never leave you.

Begin Now or Start Over

Clean the slate, God, so we can start the day fresh! Keep me from stupid sins, from thinking I can take over your work; then I can start this day sun-washed, scrubbed clean of the grime of sin. These are the words in my mouth; these are what I chew on and pray. Accept them when I place them on the morning altar, O God, my Altar-Rock, God, Priest-of-My-Altar. (Ps. 19:12–14 MSG)

God, make a fresh start in me, shape a Genesis week from the chaos of my life. (Ps. 51:10 MSG)

The LORD gave another message to Jeremiah. He said, "Go down to the potter's shop, and I will speak to you there." So I did as he told me and found the potter working at his wheel. But the jar he was making did not turn out as he had hoped, so he crushed it into a lump of clay again and started over. Then the LORD gave me this message: "O Israel, can I not do to you as this potter has done to his clay? As the clay is in the potter's hand, so are you in my hand." (Jer. 18:1–6 NLT)

O Israel, come back! Return to your GOD! You're down but you're not out. Prepare your confession and come back to GOD. Pray to him, "Take away our sin, accept our confession. Receive as restitution our repentant prayers." (Hos. 14:1–2 MSG)

Since you have heard about Jesus and have learned the truth that comes from him, throw off your old sinful nature and your former way of life, which is corrupted by lust and deception. Instead, let the Spirit renew your thoughts and attitudes. Put on your new nature, created to be like God—truly righteous and holy. (Eph. 4:21–24 NLT)

Tidbits & Morsels: If you binge, there's no upside to beating yourself up. Just start over again.

Behavior & Lifestyle

God, who gets invited to dinner at your place? How do we get on your guest list? "Walk straight, act right, tell the truth. Don't hurt your friend, don't blame your neighbor; despise the despicable. Keep your word even when it costs you, make an honest living, never take a bribe. You'll never get blacklisted if you live like this." (Ps. 15:1–5 MSG)

The end of the matter; all has been heard. Fear God and keep his commandments, for this is the whole duty of man. (Eccl. 12:13 ESV)

So here's what I want you to do, God helping you: Take your everyday, ordinary life—your sleeping, eating, going-to-work, and walking-around life—and place it before God as an offering. Embracing what God does for you is the best thing you can do for him. Don't become so well-adjusted to your culture that you fit into it without even thinking. Instead, fix your attention on God. You'll be changed from the inside out. Readily recognize what he wants from you, and quickly respond to it. Unlike the culture around you, always dragging you down to its level of immaturity, God brings the best out of you, develops well-formed maturity in you. (Rom. 12:1–2 MSG)

Do not be slothful in zeal, be fervent in spirit, serve the Lord. Rejoice in hope, be patient in tribulation, be constant in prayer. (Rom. 12:11–12 ESV)

Live creatively, friends. If someone falls into sin, forgivingly restore him, saving your critical comments for yourself. You might be needing forgiveness before the day's out. Stoop down and reach out to those who

> are oppressed. Share their burdens, and so complete Christ's law. If you think you are too good for that, you are badly deceived. ... Be very sure now, you who have been trained to a self-sufficient maturity, that you enter into a generous common life with those who have trained you, sharing all the good things that you have and experience. (Gal. 6:1–3, 6 MSG)

Tidbits & Morsels: Use a bread plate instead of dinner plate, a cup instead of a bowl, a teaspoon instead of a tablespoon. Get the idea?

____

____

____

Blame Others

> And they [Adam and Eve] heard the sound of the Lord God walking in the garden in the cool of the day, and Adam and his wife hid themselves from the presence of the Lord God among the trees of the garden. Then the Lord God called to Adam and said to him, "Where are you?" So he said, "I heard Your voice in the garden, and I was afraid because I was naked; and I hid myself." And He said, "Who told you that you were naked? Have you eaten from the tree of which I commanded you that you should not eat?" Then the man said, "The woman whom You gave to be with me, she gave me of the tree, and I ate." And the Lord God said to the woman, "What is this you have done?" The woman said, "The serpent deceived me, and I ate." (Gen. 3:8–13 NKJV)

> Don't blame fate when things go wrong—trouble doesn't come from nowhere. It's human! Mortals are born and bred for trouble, as certainly as sparks fly upward. (Job 5:6–7 MSG)

> A person's own folly leads to their ruin, yet their heart

rages against the Lord. (Prov. 19:3 NIV)

Don't point your finger at someone else and try to pass the blame to him! (Hos. 4:4 TLB)

[Jesus] Walking down the street, Jesus saw a man blind from birth. His disciples asked, "Rabbi, who sinned: this man or his parents, causing him to be born blind?" Jesus said, "You're asking the wrong question. You're looking for someone to blame. There is no such cause-effect here. Look instead for what God can do." (John 9:1–4 MSG)

Tidbits & Morsels: Placing blame is lame. What you eat is always your decision.

____

____

____

Boast & Brag

Let someone else praise you, not your own mouth—a stranger, not your own lips. (Prov. 27:2 NLT)

Don't shoot off your mouth or speak before you think. Don't be too quick to tell God what you think he wants to hear. (Eccl. 5:2 MSG)

This is what the Lord says: "Let not the wise boast of their wisdom or the strong boast of their strength or the rich boast of their riches, but let the one who boasts boast about this: that they have the understanding to know me, that I am the Lord, who exercises kindness, justice and righteousness on earth, for in these I delight," declares the Lord. (Jer. 9:23–24 NIV)

As the Scriptures say, "If anyone is going to boast, let him boast about what the Lord has done and not

> about himself." When someone boasts about himself and how well he has done, it doesn't count for much. But when the Lord commends him, that's different! (2 Cor. 10:17–18 TLB)

> If I [Paul] must boast, I will boast of the things that show my weakness. (2 Cor. 11:30 ESV)

Tidbits & Morsels: Be vigilant. Pride is waiting to pounce with every pound lost.

____

____

____

Bondage or Slavery

> [Jesus] Truly, truly, I say to you, everyone who practices sin is a slave to sin. The slave does not remain in the house forever; the son remains forever. So if the Son sets you free, you will be free indeed. (John 8:34–36 ESV)

> As long as you did what you felt like doing, ignoring God, you didn't have to bother with right thinking or right living, or right anything for that matter. But do you call that a free life? What did you get out of it? Nothing you're proud of now. Where did it get you? A dead end. But now that you've found you don't have to listen to sin tell you what to do and have discovered the delight of listening to God telling you, what a surprise! A whole, healed, put-together life right now, with more and more of life on the way! Work hard for sin your whole life and your pension is death. But God's gift is real life, eternal life, delivered by Jesus, our Master. (Rom. 6:20–23 MSG)

> "I have the right to do anything," you say—but not

everything is beneficial. "I have the right to do anything"—but I will not be mastered by anything." (1 Cor. 6:12 NIV)

Formerly, when you did not know God, you were enslaved to those that by nature are not gods. But now that you have come to know God, or rather to be known by God, how can you turn back again to the weak and worthless elementary principles of the world, whose slaves you want to be once more? (Gal. 4:8–9 ESV)

They promise them freedom, but they themselves are slaves of corruption. For whatever overcomes a person, to that he is enslaved. For if, after they have escaped the defilements of the world through the knowledge of our Lord and Savior Jesus Christ, they are again entangled in them and overcome, the last state has become worse for them than the first. For it would have been better for them never to have known the way of righteousness than after knowing it to turn back from the holy commandment delivered to them. What the true proverb says has happened to them: "The dog returns to its own vomit, and the sow, after washing herself, returns to wallow in the mire." (2 Pet. 2:19–22 ESV)

Tidbits & Morsels: Nix the legalistic "all or nothing" and "fasting or gorging" extremes of eating.

___

___

___

Boredom

Instead of honoring me, you profane me. You profane me when you say, "Worship is not important, and what we bring to worship is of no account," and when you say, "I'm bored—this doesn't do anything for me." You act so superior, sticking your noses in the air—act

> superior to me, GOD-of-the-Angel-Armies! And when you do offer something to me, it's a hand-me-down, or broken, or useless. Do you think I'm going to accept it? This is GOD speaking to you! (Mal. 1:12–13 MSG)

> Look carefully then how you walk, not as unwise but as wise, making the best use of the time, because the days are evil. (Eph. 5:15–16 ESV)

> And we are anxious that you keep right on loving others as long as life lasts, so that you will get your full reward. Then, knowing what lies ahead for you, you won't become bored with being a Christian nor become spiritually dull and indifferent, but you will be anxious to follow the example of those who receive all that God has promised them because of their strong faith and patience. (Heb. 6:11–12 TLB)

Tidbits & Morsels: The best antidote for boredom is to help someone in need.

____

____

____

BUDDY UP OR PARTNER

> But Moses' hands grew weary, so they took a stone and put it under him, and he sat on it, while Aaron and Hur held up his hands, one on one side, and the other on the other side. So his hands were steady until the going down of the sun. (Ex. 17:12 ESV)

> As iron sharpens iron, so one person sharpens another. (Prov. 27:17 NIV)

> Two are better than one, because they have a good reward for their toil. For if they fall, one will lift up his fellow. But woe to him who is alone when he falls

> and has not another to lift him up! ... And though a man might prevail against one who is alone, two will withstand him—a threefold cord is not quickly broken. (Eccl. 4:9–10, 12 ESV)

> [Jesus] After these things the Lord appointed seventy others also, and sent them two by two before His face into every city and place where He Himself was about to go. (Luke 10:1 NKJV)

> Don't team up with those who are unbelievers. How can righteousness be a partner with wickedness? How can light live with darkness? What harmony can there be between Christ and the devil? How can a believer be a partner with an unbeliever? (2 Cor. 6:14–15 NLT)

Tidbits & Morsels: Be honest and transparent with your accountability partners. Don't waste their time or yours.

Busyness

> It's useless to rise early and go to bed late and work your worried fingers to the bone. Don't you know he enjoys giving rest to those he loves? (Ps. 127:2 MSG)

> Tell my people what's wrong with their lives, face my family Jacob with their sins! They're busy, busy, busy at worship, and love studying all about me. To all appearances they're a nation of right-living people—law-abiding, God-honoring. They ask me, "What's the right thing to do?" and love having me on their side. But they also complain, "Why do we fast and you don't look our way? Why do we humble ourselves and you don't even notice?" Well, here's why: "The bottom line on your 'fast days' is profit." (Isa. 58:1–3 MSG)

> [Jesus] Now it happened as they went that He entered a certain village; and a certain woman named Martha welcomed Him into her house. And she had a sister called Mary, who also sat at Jesus' feet and heard His word. But Martha was distracted with much serving, and she approached Him and said, "Lord, do You not care that my sister has left me to serve alone? Therefore tell her to help me." And Jesus answered and said to her, "Martha, Martha, you are worried and troubled about many things. But one thing is needed, and Mary has chosen that good part, which will not be taken away from her." (Luke 10:38–42 NKJV)

> Don't waste your time on useless work, mere busywork, the barren pursuits of darkness. Expose these things for the sham they are. It's a scandal when people waste their lives on things they must do in the darkness where no one will see. Rip the cover off those frauds and see how attractive they look in the light of Christ. Wake up from your sleep, climb out of your coffins; Christ will show you the light! So watch your step. Use your head. Make the most of every chance you get. These are desperate times! (Eph. 5:11–16 MSG)

Tidbits & Morsels: Has the pace of life gotten away from you? Hit the brakes to ponder, process, and appreciate each moment.

____

____

____

Celebrate Achievements

> Then Moses said to the people, "Commemorate this day, the day you came out of Egypt, out of the land of slavery, because the Lord brought you out of it with a mighty hand." (Ex. 13:3 NIV)

> Feast there in the Presence of GOD, your God. Celebrate everything that you and your families have accomplished under the blessing of GOD, your God. (Deut. 12:7 MSG)

> Nehemiah said, "Go and enjoy choice food and sweet drinks, and send some to those who have nothing prepared. This day is holy to our Lord. Do not grieve, for the joy of the LORD is your strength." The Levites calmed all the people, saying, "Be still, for this is a holy day. Do not grieve." Then all the people went away to eat and drink, to send portions of food and to celebrate with great joy, because they now understood the words that had been made known to them. (Neh. 8:10–12 NIV)

> For everything there is a season, and a time for every matter under heaven: ... a time to weep, and a time to laugh; a time to mourn, and a time to dance. (Eccl. 3:1, 4 ESV)

> Do not despise these small beginnings, for the LORD rejoices to see the work begin, to see the plumb line in Zerubbabel's hand. (Zech. 4:10 NLT)

Tidbits & Morsels: No matter how great or how small, celebrate each achievement with your own "stones of remembrance."

____

____

____

Cheat or Eat in Secret

> Mark well that GOD doesn't miss a move you make; he's aware of every step you take. The shadow of your sin will overtake you; you'll find yourself stumbling all over yourself in the dark. (Prov. 5:21–22 MSG)

> Bread gained by deceit is sweet to a man, but afterward his mouth will be full of gravel. (Prov. 20:17 ESV)

> God will judge us for everything we do, including every secret thing, whether good or bad. (Eccl. 12:14 NLT)

> Catch for us the foxes, the little foxes that ruin the vineyards, our vineyards that are in bloom. (Song 2:15 NIV)

> "Am I only a God nearby," declares the LORD, "and not a God far away? Who can hide in secret places so that I cannot see them?" declares the LORD. "Do not I fill heaven and earth?" declares the LORD. (Jer. 23:23–24 NIV)

> For nothing is secret that will not be revealed, nor anything hidden that will not be known and come to light. (Luke 8:17 NKJV)

Tidbits & Morsels: Just so you know, eating in secret still counts as eating.

____

____

____

Clean Plate Club vs. Leftovers

> At mealtime Boaz said to her [Ruth], "Come over here. Have some bread and dip it in the wine vinegar." When she sat down with the harvesters, he offered her some roasted grain. She ate all she wanted and had some left over. ... So Ruth gleaned in the field until evening. Then she threshed the barley she had gathered, and it amounted to about an ephah. She carried it back to town, and her mother-in-law saw how much she had gathered. Ruth also brought out and gave her what she had left over after she had eaten enough. (Ruth 2:14, 17–18 NIV)

> But Elisha answered, "Give it to the people to eat. For this is what the LORD says: 'They will eat and have some

left over.'" Then he set it before them, and they ate and had some left over, according to the word of the LORD. (2 Kings 4:43–44 NIV)

The crowd ate its fill. Seven sacks of leftovers were collected. (Mark 8:8 MSG)

[Jesus] Then Jesus took the bread and, having given thanks, gave it to those who were seated. He did the same with the fish. All ate as much as they wanted. When the people had eaten their fill, he said to his disciples, "Gather the leftovers so nothing is wasted." They went to work and filled twelve large baskets with leftovers from the five barley loaves. (John 6:11–13 MSG)

Tidbits & Morsels: Be a rebel! Don't clean your plate. Save some for later.

____

____

____

Codependency or Enabling

[Jesus] Then the kingdom of heaven shall be likened to ten virgins who took their lamps and went out to meet the bridegroom. Now five of them were wise, and five were foolish. Those who were foolish took their lamps and took no oil with them, but the wise took oil in their vessels with their lamps. But while the bridegroom was delayed, they all slumbered and slept. And at midnight a cry was heard: "Behold, the bridegroom is coming; go out to meet him!" Then all those virgins arose and trimmed their lamps. And the foolish said to the wise, "Give us some of your oil, for our lamps are going out." But the wise answered, saying, "No, lest there should not be enough for us and you; but go rather to those who sell, and buy for yourselves." And while they went to buy, the bridegroom came, and those who were ready

> went in with him to the wedding; and the door was shut. (Matt. 25:1–10 NKJV)

> If you preach, just preach God's Message, nothing else; if you help, just help, don't take over; if you teach, stick to your teaching; if you give encouraging guidance, be careful that you don't get bossy; if you're put in charge, don't manipulate; if you're called to give aid to people in distress, keep your eyes open and be quick to respond; if you work with the disadvantaged, don't let yourself get irritated with them or depressed by them. Keep a smile on your face. (Rom. 12:6–8 MSG)

> But let each one test his own work, and then his reason to boast will be in himself alone and not in his neighbor. For each will have to bear his own load. (Gal. 6:4–5 ESV)

> But we command you, brethren, in the name of our Lord Jesus Christ, that you withdraw from every brother who walks disorderly and not according to the tradition which he received from us. For you yourselves know how you ought to follow us, for we were not disorderly among you; nor did we eat anyone's bread free of charge, but worked with labor and toil night and day, that we might not be a burden to any of you, not because we do not have authority, but to make ourselves an example of how you should follow us. (2 Thess. 3:6–9 NKJV)

Tidbits & Morsels: Don't be the last one to realize you have a problem with food. Be as concerned about enabling yourself as you are about enabling others.

____

____

____

Common Sense

> O Lord, listen to my prayers; give me the common sense you promised. (Ps. 119:169 TLB)

> If you want favor with both God and man, and a reputation for good judgment and common sense, then trust the Lord completely; don't ever trust yourself. (Prov. 3:4–5 TLB)

> Have two goals: wisdom—that is, knowing and doing right—and common sense. Don't let them slip away, for they fill you with living energy and bring you honor and respect. They keep you safe from defeat and disaster and from stumbling off the trail. With them on guard you can sleep without fear; you need not be afraid of disaster or the plots of wicked men, for the Lord is with you; he protects you. (Prov. 3:21–26 TLB)

> Common sense and success belong to me [Wisdom]. Insight and strength are mine. (Prov. 8:14 NLT)

> Let the Word of Christ—the Message—have the run of the house. Give it plenty of room in your lives. Instruct and direct one another using good common sense. (Col. 3:16 MSG)

Tidbits & Morsels: If following a fad diet resulted in permanent weight loss, do you think the billion-dollar diet industry would want the next generation of dieters to know about this diet? Think about it. What does your common sense tell you?

____

____

____

Complain or Whine

> Then the people of Israel returned to Mount Hor, and from there continued southward along the road to the Red Sea in order to go around the land of Edom. The people were very discouraged; they began to murmur against God and to complain against Moses. "Why

> have you brought us out of Egypt to die here in the wilderness?" they whined. "There is nothing to eat here, and nothing to drink, and we hate this insipid manna." (Num. 21:4–5 TLB)

> I said to myself, I'm going to quit complaining! I'll keep quiet, especially when the ungodly are around me. (Ps. 39:1 TLB)

> And do not grumble, as some of them did—and were killed by the destroying angel. These things happened to them as examples and were written down as warnings for us, on whom the culmination of the ages has come. So, if you think you are standing firm, be careful that you don't fall! (1 Cor. 10:10–12 NIV)

> Do all things without grumbling or disputing, that you may be blameless and innocent, children of God without blemish in the midst of a crooked and twisted generation, among whom you shine as lights in the world, holding fast to the word of life, so that in the day of Christ I may be proud that I did not run in vain or labor in vain. (Phil. 2:14–16 ESV)

Tidbits & Morsels: Find the verse in the Bible that says, "God blessed the bellyachers and grumblers."

____

____

____

Confession

> When I kept silent, my bones grew old through my groaning all the day long. For day and night Your hand was heavy upon me; my vitality was turned into the drought of summer. *Selah* I acknowledged my sin to You, and my iniquity I have not hidden. I said, "I will confess my transgressions to the LORD," and You forgave the iniquity of my sin. *Selah* (Ps. 32:3–5 NKJV)

Whoever conceals his transgressions will not prosper, but he who confesses and forsakes them will obtain mercy. (Prov. 28:13 ESV)

Therefore confess your sins to each other and pray for each other so that you may be healed. The prayer of a righteous person is powerful and effective. (James 5:16 NIV)

If we claim to be without sin, we deceive ourselves and the truth is not in us. If we confess our sins, he is faithful and just and will forgive us our sins and purify us from all unrighteousness. If we claim we have not sinned, we make him out to be a liar and his word is not in us. (1 John 1:8–10 NIV)

Tidbits & Morsels: What past sin are you still fretting about or eating over? Confess it, accept God's forgiveness, then move on.

___

___

___

Confidence in God vs. Self-confidence

Many blessings are given to those who trust the Lord and have no confidence in those who are proud or who trust in idols. (Ps. 40:4 TLB)

Do not be afraid of sudden terror, nor of trouble from the wicked when it comes; for the Lord will be your confidence and will keep your foot from being caught. (Prov. 3:25–26 NKJV)

[Jesus] Jesus looked at them and said, "With man it is impossible, but not with God. For all things are possible with God." (Mark 10:27 ESV)

> We are confident of all this because of our great trust in God through Christ. It is not that we think we are qualified to do anything on our own. Our qualification comes from God. He has enabled us to be ministers of his new covenant. This is a covenant not of written laws, but of the Spirit. The old written covenant ends in death; but under the new covenant, the Spirit gives life. (2 Cor. 3:4–6 NLT)

> So do not throw away this confident trust in the Lord. Remember the great reward it brings you! (Heb. 10:35 NLT)

> If our hearts condemn us, we know that God is greater than our hearts, and he knows everything. Dear friends, if our hearts do not condemn us, we have confidence before God and receive from him anything we ask, because we keep his commands and do what pleases him. (1 John 3:20–22 NIV)

Tidbits & Morsels: Put confidence in God not in yourself—which is the only safe choice.

____

____

____

Confusion

> Still, when I tried to figure it out [why the wicked have it made], all I got was a splitting headache ... until I entered the sanctuary of God. Then I saw the whole picture: The slippery road you've put them on, with a final crash in a ditch of delusions. (Ps. 73:16–18 MSG)

> Since earliest times men have seen the earth and sky and all God made and have known of his existence and great eternal power. So they will have no excuse

when they stand before God at Judgment Day. Yes, they knew about him all right, but they wouldn't admit it or worship him or even thank him for all his daily care. And after a while they began to think up silly ideas of what God was like and what he wanted them to do. The result was that their foolish minds became dark and confused. Claiming themselves to be wise without God, they became utter fools instead. (Rom. 1:20–22 TLB)

Now we see things imperfectly, like puzzling reflections in a mirror, but then we will see everything with perfect clarity. All that I know now is partial and incomplete, but then I will know everything completely, just as God now knows me completely. (1 Cor. 13:12 NLT)

For God is not a God of confusion but of peace. (1 Cor. 14:33 ESV)

We are pressed on every side by troubles, but we are not crushed. We are perplexed, but not driven to despair. (2 Cor. 4:8 NLT)

I am astonished that you are so quickly deserting the one who called you to live in the grace of Christ and are turning to a different gospel—which is really no gospel at all. Evidently some people are throwing you into confusion and are trying to pervert the gospel of Christ. But even if we or an angel from heaven should preach a gospel other than the one we preached to you, let them be under God's curse! (Gal. 1:6–8 NIV)

Tidbits & Morsels: Trying to control everything in your life leads to confusion and frustration, which affects how you eat—and seldom in a good way.

____

____

____

Conscience

> So I [Paul] always take pains to have a clear conscience toward both God and man. (Acts 24:16 ESV)

> He will punish sin wherever it is found. He will punish the heathen when they sin, even though they never had God's written laws, for down in their hearts they know right from wrong. God's laws are written within them; their own conscience accuses them, or sometimes excuses them. And God will punish the Jews for sinning because they have his written laws but don't obey them. They know what is right but don't do it. After all, salvation is not given to those who know what to do, unless they do it. (Rom. 2:12–15 TLB)

> Eat anything sold in the meat market without raising questions of conscience, for, "The earth is the Lord's, and everything in it." If an unbeliever invites you to a meal and you want to go, eat whatever is put before you without raising questions of conscience. But if someone says to you, "This has been offered in sacrifice," then do not eat it, both for the sake of the one who told you and for the sake of conscience. (1 Cor. 10:25–28 NIV)

> Everything is pure to those whose hearts are pure. But nothing is pure to those who are corrupt and unbelieving, because their minds and consciences are corrupted. (Titus 1:15 NLT)

> Under the old system, the blood of goats and bulls and the ashes of a heifer could cleanse people's bodies from ceremonial impurity. Just think how much more the blood of Christ will purify our consciences from sinful deeds so that we can worship the living God. For by the power of the eternal Spirit, Christ offered himself to God as a perfect sacrifice for our sins. (Heb. 9:13–14 NLT)

Tidbits & Morsels: If your conscience is clear, you won't hear a peep out of it.

Consequences

At the words, "Chest of God," Eli fell backward off his stool where he sat next to the gate. Eli was an old man and very fat. When he fell, he broke his neck and died. (1 Sam. 4:18 MSG)

Can a man scoop fire into his lap without his clothes being burned? Can a man walk on hot coals without his feet being scorched? (Prov. 6:27–28 NIV)

A prudent person foresees danger and takes precautions. The simpleton goes blindly on and suffers the consequences. (Prov. 27:12 NLT)

[Jesus] But everyone who hears these words of mine and does not put them into practice is like a foolish man who built his house on sand. The rain came down, the streams rose, and the winds blew and beat against that house, and it fell with a great crash. (Matt. 7:26–27 NIV)

If you go against the grain, you get splinters, regardless of which neighborhood you're from, what your parents taught you, what schools you attended. But if you embrace the way God does things, there are wonderful payoffs, again without regard to where you are from or how you were brought up. Being a Jew won't give you an automatic stamp of approval. God pays no attention to what others say (or what you think) about you. He makes up his own mind. (Rom. 2:9–11 MSG)

Do not be deceived: God is not mocked, for whatever one sows, that will he also reap. For the one who sows to his own flesh will from the flesh reap corruption, but the one who sows to the Spirit will from the Spirit reap eternal life. (Gal. 6:7–8 ESV)

Tidbits & Morsels: You know those crusts you cut off your kids' sandwiches? Yeah, ... stop eating them.

CONTENTMENT & SATISFACTION

> GOD, I'm not trying to rule the roost, I don't want to be king of the mountain. I haven't meddled where I have no business or fantasized grandiose plans. I've kept my feet on the ground, I've cultivated a quiet heart. Like a baby content in its mother's arms, my soul is a baby content. (Ps. 131:1–2 MSG)

> Two things I ask of you; deny them not to me before I die: Remove far from me falsehood and lying; give me neither poverty nor riches; feed me with the food that is needful for me, lest I be full and deny you and say, "Who is the LORD?" or lest I be poor and steal and profane the name of my God. (Prov. 30:7–9 ESV)

> So I decided there is nothing better than to enjoy food and drink and to find satisfaction in work. Then I realized that these pleasures are from the hand of God. For who can eat or enjoy anything apart from him? (Eccl. 2:24–25 NLT)

> I [Paul] am not saying this because I am in need, for I have learned to be content whatever the circumstances. I know what it is to be in need, and I know what it is to have plenty. I have learned the secret of being content in any and every situation, whether well fed or hungry, whether living in plenty or in want. I can do all this through him who gives me strength. (Phil. 4:11–13 NIV)

> But godliness with contentment is great gain, for we brought nothing into the world, and we cannot take

anything out of the world. But if we have food and clothing, with these we will be content. (1 Tim. 6:6–8 ESV)

Keep a sharp eye out for weeds of bitter discontent. A thistle or two gone to seed can ruin a whole garden in no time. Watch out for the Esau syndrome: trading away God's lifelong gift in order to satisfy a short-term appetite. You well know how Esau later regretted that impulsive act and wanted God's blessing—but by then it was too late, tears or no tears. (Heb. 12:15–17 MSG)

Tidbits & Morsels: Though contentment and satisfaction may not sound as exciting as whitewater rafting, they arrive on a river of peace and joy.

Conviction

For I am ready to fall, and my pain is ever before me. I confess my iniquity; I am sorry for my sin. (Ps. 38:17–18 ESV)

When troubles ganged up on me, a mob of sins past counting, I was so swamped by guilt I couldn't see my way clear. More guilt in my heart than hair on my head, so heavy the guilt that my heart gave out. (Ps. 40:12 MSG)

[Jesus] And this is the condemnation, that the light has come into the world, and men loved darkness rather than light, because their deeds were evil. For everyone practicing evil hates the light and does not come to the light, lest his deeds should be exposed. But he who does the truth comes to the light, that his deeds may

> be clearly seen, that they have been done in God. (John 3:19–21 NKJV)
>
> You let the distress bring you to God, not drive you from him. The result was all gain, no loss. Distress that drives us to God does that. It turns us around. It gets us back in the way of salvation. We never regret that kind of pain. But those who let distress drive them away from God are full of regrets, end up on a deathbed of regrets. And now, isn't it wonderful all the ways in which this distress has goaded you closer to God? You're more alive, more concerned, more sensitive, more reverent, more human, more passionate, more responsible. Looked at from any angle, you've come out of this with purity of heart. (2 Cor. 7:9–11 MSG)

Tidbits & Morsels: Compared to conviction, confession is a piece of cake.

____

____

____

Correction & Discipline

> So be very careful to act exactly as God commands you. Don't veer off to the right or the left. Walk straight down the road God commands so that you'll have a good life and live a long time in the land that you're about to possess. (Deut. 5:32–33 MSG)
>
> But don't, dear friend, resent God's discipline; don't sulk under his loving correction. It's the child he loves that God corrects; a father's delight is behind all this. (Prov. 3:10–12 MSG)
>
> Whoever heeds instruction is on the path to life, but he who rejects reproof leads others astray. (Prov. 10:17 ESV)

If you love learning, you love the discipline that goes with it—how shortsighted to refuse correction! (Prov. 12:1 MSG)

A word fitly spoken is like apples of gold in a setting of silver. Like a gold ring or an ornament of gold is a wise reprover to a listening ear. (Prov. 25:11–12 ESV)

But I discipline my body and bring it into subjection, lest, when I have preached to others, I myself should become disqualified. (1 Cor. 9:27 NKJV)

Our earthly fathers trained us for a few brief years, doing the best for us that they knew how, but God's correction is always right and for our best good, that we may share his holiness. Being punished isn't enjoyable while it is happening—it hurts! But afterwards we can see the result, a quiet growth in grace and character. So take a new grip with your tired hands, stand firm on your shaky legs, and mark out a straight, smooth path for your feet so that those who follow you, though weak and lame, will not fall and hurt themselves but become strong. (Heb. 12:10–13 TLB)

Tidbits & Morsels: The fruit of correction and discipline has a sweet aftertaste.

____

____

____

Count It All Joy

Oh, what joy for those whose disobedience is forgiven, whose sin is put out of sight! Yes, what joy for those whose record the Lord has cleared of guilt, whose lives are lived in complete honesty! (Ps. 32:1–2 NLT)

In the day of prosperity be joyful, and in the day of adversity consider: God has made the one as well as the other, so that man may not find out anything that will be after him. (Eccl. 7:14 ESV)

Though the fig tree does not bud and there are no grapes on the vines, though the olive crop fails and the fields produce no food, though there are no sheep in the pen and no cattle in the stalls, yet I will rejoice in the LORD, I will be joyful in God my Savior. (Hab. 3:17–18 NIV)

Although great trouble accompanied the Word, you were able to take great joy from the Holy Spirit!—taking the trouble with the joy, the joy with the trouble. (1 Thess. 1:6 MSG)

Count it all joy, my brothers, when you meet trials of various kinds, for you know that the testing of your faith produces steadfastness. And let steadfastness have its full effect, that you may be perfect and complete, lacking in nothing. (James 1:2–4 ESV)

Tidbits & Morsels: If you can't find the joy in something, you can always find the joy in Someone!

____

____

____

Count the Cost

It is foolish and rash to make a promise to the Lord before counting the cost. (Prov. 20:25 TLB)

The wicked put up a bold front, but the upright give thought to their ways. (Prov. 21:29 NIV)

[Jesus] When He had called the people to Himself, with His disciples also, He said to them, "Whoever desires

> to come after Me, let him deny himself, and take up his cross, and follow Me. For whoever desires to save his life will lose it, but whoever loses his life for My sake and the gospel's will save it. For what will it profit a man if he gains the whole world, and loses his own soul?" (Mark 8:34–36 NKJV)

> [Jesus] Is there anyone here who, planning to build a new house, doesn't first sit down and figure the cost so you'll know if you can complete it? If you only get the foundation laid and then run out of money, you're going to look pretty foolish. Everyone passing by will poke fun at you: "He started something he couldn't finish." Or can you imagine a king going into battle against another king without first deciding whether it is possible with his ten thousand troops to face the twenty thousand troops of the other? And if he decides he can't, won't he send an emissary and work out a truce? Simply put, if you're not willing to take what is dearest to you, whether plans or people, and kiss it good-bye, you can't be my disciple. (Luke 14:28–33 MSG)

Tidbits & Morsels: Count the big and little things—steps, pounds, and bites.

____

____

____

Count Your Blessings

> Now it shall come to pass, if you diligently obey the voice of the Lord your God, to observe carefully all His commandments which I command you today, that the Lord your God will set you high above all nations of the earth. And all these blessings shall come upon you and overtake you, because you obey the voice of

> the LORD your God: Blessed shall you be in the city and blessed shall you be in the country. Blessed shall be the fruit of your body, the produce of your ground and the increase of your herds, the increase of your cattle and the offspring of your flocks. Blessed shall be your basket and your kneading bowl. Blessed shall you be when you come in and, blessed shall you be when you go out. (Deut. 28:1–6 NKJV)

> You provide delicious food for me in the presence of my enemies. You have welcomed me as your guest; blessings overflow! (Ps. 23:5 TLB)

> GOD's blessing makes life rich; nothing we do can improve on God. (Prov. 10:22 MSG)

> [Jesus] You're blessed when you're at the end of your rope. With less of you there is more of God and his rule. You're blessed when you feel you've lost what is most dear to you. Only then can you be embraced by the One most dear to you. You're blessed when you're content with just who you are—no more, no less. That's the moment you find yourselves proud owners of everything that can't be bought. (Matt. 5:3–5 MSG)

> For as you know him better, he will give you, through his great power, everything you need for living a truly good life: he even shares his own glory and his own goodness with us! And by that same mighty power he has given us all the other rich and wonderful blessings he promised; for instance, the promise to save us from the lust and rottenness all around us, and to give us his own character. (2 Pet. 1:3–4 TLB)

Tidbits & Morsels: Count your blessings one by one; it will take you a lifetime.

___

___

___

Cravings & Withdrawals

The misfits among the people had a craving and soon they had the People of Israel whining, "Why can't we have meat? We ate fish in Egypt—and got it free!—to say nothing of the cucumbers and melons, the leeks and onions and garlic. But nothing tastes good out here; all we get is manna, manna, manna." (Num. 11:4–6 MSG)

When the Lord your God has enlarged your territory as he promised you, and you crave meat and say, "I would like some meat," then you may eat as much of it as you want. (Deut. 12:20 NIV)

But they soon forgot his works; they did not wait for his counsel. But they had a wanton craving in the wilderness and put God to the test in the desert; he gave them what they asked, but sent a wasting disease among them. (Ps. 106:13–15 ESV)

I say then: Walk in the Spirit, and you shall not fulfill the lust of the flesh. For the flesh lusts against the Spirit, and the Spirit against the flesh; and these are contrary to one another, so that you do not do the things that you wish. But if you are led by the Spirit, you are not under the law. (Gal. 5:16–18 NKJV)

Like newborn babies, crave pure spiritual milk, so that by it you may grow up in your salvation, now that you have tasted that the Lord is good. (1 Pet. 2:2–3 NIV)

Since Jesus went through everything you're going through and more, learn to think like him. Think of your sufferings as a weaning from that old sinful habit of always expecting to get your own way. Then you'll be able to live out your days free to pursue what God wants instead of being tyrannized by what you want. (1 Pet. 4:1–2 MSG)

Tidbits & Morsels: If you forever ban the foods you enjoy, you may crave them more. Sometimes—not all the time—cravings and withdrawals signify something your body needs.

____

____

____

Denial or Deluded Thinking

You rabble—how long do I put up with your scorn? How long will you lust after lies? How long will you live crazed by illusion? (Ps. 4:2 MSG)

There is a way that seems right to a man, but its end is the way to death. (Prov. 16:25 ESV)

You can't heal a wound by saying it's not there! Yet the priests and prophets give assurances of peace when all is war. (Jer. 6:14 TLB)

[Jesus] Everyone who makes a practice of doing evil, addicted to denial and illusion, hates God-light and won't come near it, fearing a painful exposure. But anyone working and living in truth and reality welcomes God-light so the work can be seen for the God-work it is. (John 3:20–21 MSG)

You're going to find that there will be times when people will have no stomach for solid teaching, but will fill up on spiritual junk food—catchy opinions that tickle their fancy. They'll turn their backs on truth and chase mirages. But you—keep your eye on what you're doing; accept the hard times along with the good; keep the Message alive; do a thorough job as God's servant. (2 Tim. 4:3–5 MSG)

It wasn't so long ago that we ourselves were stupid and stubborn, easy marks for sin, ordered every which way by our glands, going around with a chip on our shoulder, hated and hating back. But when God, our kind and loving Savior God, stepped in, he saved us from all that. (Titus 3:3–5 MSG)

So we are lying if we say we have fellowship with God but go on living in spiritual darkness; we are not practicing the truth. (1 John 1:6 NLT)

Tidbits & Morsels: You begin walking down the candy aisle at the food store. Your conscience pokes you. Irritated, you respond, "I'm just looking." For what? Trouble?

____

____

____

Depression or Discouragement

Then Job answered and said: "Oh that my vexation were weighed, and all my calamity laid in the balances! For then it would be heavier than the sand of the sea; therefore my words have been rash. For the arrows of the Almighty are in me; my spirit drinks their poison; the terrors of God are arrayed against me." (Job 6:1–4 ESV)

Yes, the Lord hears the good man when he calls to him for help and saves him out of all his troubles. The Lord is close to those whose hearts are breaking; he rescues those who are humbly sorry for their sins. (Ps. 34:17–18 TLB)

I am completely discouraged—I lie in the dust. Revive me by your Word. (Ps. 119:25 TLB)

Then Jonah prayed to the LORD his God from inside the fish. He said: "... As my life was slipping away, I remembered the LORD. And my earnest prayer went out

> to you in your holy Temple. Those who worship false gods turn their backs on all God's mercies. But I will offer sacrifices to you with songs of praise, and I will fulfill all my vows. For my salvation comes from the LORD alone." (Jonah 2:1–2, 7–9 NLT)

> We [Paul & Timothy] faced conflict from every direction, with battles on the outside and fear on the inside. But God, who encourages those who are discouraged, encouraged us by the arrival of Titus. His presence was a joy, but so was the news he brought of the encouragement he received from you. (2 Cor. 7:5–7 NLT)

Tidbits & Morsels: Fight discouragement by speaking God's encouraging Word out loud!

___

___

___

Determination or Resolve

> When you go to war against your enemy and see horses and chariots and soldiers far outnumbering you, do not recoil in fear of them; GOD, your God, who brought you up out of Egypt is with you. When the battle is about to begin, let the priest come forward and speak to the troops. He'll say, "Attention, Israel. In a few minutes you're going to do battle with your enemies. Don't waver in resolve. Don't fear. Don't hesitate. Don't panic. GOD, your God, is right there with you, fighting with you against your enemies, fighting to win." (Deut. 20:1–4 MSG)

> Strengthen your resolve and do what must be done. (2 Sam. 2:7 MSG)

> For Ezra had set his heart to study the Law of the LORD, and to do it and to teach his statutes and rules in Israel. (Ezra 7:10 ESV)

> I have chosen to be faithful; I have determined to live by your regulations. (Ps. 119:30 NLT)

> But Daniel was determined not to defile himself by eating the food and wine given to them by the king. He asked the chief of staff for permission not to eat these unacceptable foods. (Dan. 1:8 NLT)

Tidbits & Morsels: Dining out is fine—but wisdom strongly suggests you stay away from all-you-can-eat buffets. Not kidding.

____

____

____

Discernment

> The wisdom of the prudent is to discern his way, but the folly of fools is deceiving. (Prov. 14:8 ESV)

> But it was to us that God revealed these things by his Spirit. For his Spirit searches out everything and shows us God's deep secrets. No one can know a person's thoughts except that person's own spirit, and no one can know God's thoughts except God's own Spirit. And we have received God's Spirit (not the world's spirit), so we can know the wonderful things God has freely given us. When we tell you these things, we do not use words that come from human wisdom. Instead, we speak words given to us by the Spirit, using the Spirit's words to explain spiritual truths. But people who aren't spiritual can't receive these truths from God's Spirit. It all sounds foolish to them, and they can't understand it, for only those who are spiritual can understand what the Spirit means. (1 Cor. 2:10–14 NLT)

> But I do more than thank. I ask—ask the God of our Master, Jesus Christ, the God of glory—to make you

> intelligent and discerning in knowing him personally, your eyes focused and clear, so that you can see exactly what it is he is calling you to do, grasp the immensity of this glorious way of life he has for his followers, oh, the utter extravagance of his work in us who trust him—endless energy, boundless strength! (Eph. 1:17–19 MSG)

> And it is my prayer that your love may abound more and more, with knowledge and all discernment, so that you may approve what is excellent, and so be pure and blameless for the day of Christ, filled with the fruit of righteousness that comes through Jesus Christ, to the glory and praise of God. (Phil. 1:9–11 ESV)

> Do not quench the Spirit. Do not despise prophecies, but test everything; hold fast what is good. Abstain from every form of evil. (1 Thess. 5:19–22 ESV)

Tidbits & Morsels: Just because your mouth feels like chewing doesn't mean your stomach needs food.

____

____

____

Doubt

> [Jesus] And Peter answered him, "Lord, if it is you, command me to come to you on the water." He [Jesus] said, "Come." So Peter got out of the boat and walked on the water and came to Jesus. But when he saw the wind, he was afraid, and beginning to sink he cried out, "Lord, save me." Jesus immediately reached out his hand and took hold of him, saying to him, "O you of little faith, why did you doubt?" (Matt. 14:28–31 ESV)

> [Jesus] He asked the boy's father, "How long has this been going on?" "Ever since he was a little boy. Many times it pitches him into fire or the river to do away with him. If you can do anything, do it. Have a heart

and help us!" Jesus said, "If? There are no 'ifs' among believers. Anything can happen." No sooner were the words out of his mouth than the father cried, "Then I believe. Help me with my doubts!" (Mark 9:21–24 MSG)

[Jesus] "Why are you frightened?" he asked. "Why do you doubt that it is really I? Look at my hands! Look at my feet! You can see that it is I, myself! Touch me and make sure that I am not a ghost! For ghosts don't have bodies, as you see that I do!" As he spoke, he held out his hands for them to see the marks of the nails and showed them the wounds in his feet. Still they stood there undecided, filled with joy and doubt. (Luke 24:38–41 TLB)

If any of you lacks wisdom, you should ask God, who gives generously to all without finding fault, and it will be given to you. But when you ask, you must believe and not doubt, because the one who doubts is like a wave of the sea, blown and tossed by the wind. That person should not expect to receive anything from the Lord. Such a person is double-minded and unstable in all they do. (James 1:5–8 NIV)

Tidbits & Morsels: Do you doubt the food will still be on your plate if you put your fork down between bites? When in doubt, leave it out ... of your mouth.

____

____

____

Easy Does It

A wise man is cautious and avoids danger; a fool plunges ahead with great confidence. (Prov. 14:16 TLB)

> The one who knows much says little; an understanding person remains calm. (Prov. 17:27 MSG)

> Steady plodding brings prosperity; hasty speculation brings poverty. (Prov. 21:5 TLB)

> To everything there is a season, a time for every purpose under heaven: A time to be born, and a time to die; a time to plant, and a time to pluck what is planted; a time to kill, and a time to heal; a time to break down, and a time to build up; a time to weep, and a time to laugh; a time to mourn, and a time to dance; a time to cast away stones, and a time to gather stones; a time to embrace, and a time to refrain from embracing; a time to gain, and a time to lose; a time to keep, and a time to throw away; a time to tear, and a time to sew; a time to keep silence, and a time to speak; a time to love, and a time to hate; a time of war, and a time of peace. (Eccl. 3:1–8 NKJV)

> The path of right-living people is level. The Leveler evens the road for the right-living. We're in no hurry, God. We're content to linger in the path sign-posted with your decisions. (Isa. 26:7–8 MSG)

Tidbits & Morsels: What's your hurry? Eat mindfully and chew slowly, so you don't pass by satisfaction and run into discomfort.

____

____

____

Empowerment

> The Lord says, "I will make my people strong with power from me! They will go wherever they wish, and wherever they go they will be under my personal care." (Zech. 10:12 TLB)

> [Jesus] One day Jesus called together his twelve disciples and gave them power and authority to cast out all demons and to heal all diseases. (Luke 9:1 NLT)

> With the arrival of Jesus, the Messiah, that fateful dilemma is resolved. Those who enter into Christ's being-here-for-us no longer have to live under a continuous, low-lying black cloud. A new power is in operation. The Spirit of life in Christ, like a strong wind, has magnificently cleared the air, freeing you from a fated lifetime of brutal tyranny at the hands of sin and death. (Rom. 8:1–2 MSG)

> For the kingdom of God does not consist in talk but in power. (1 Cor. 4:20 ESV)

> I pray that from his glorious, unlimited resources he will empower you with inner strength through his Spirit. Then Christ will make his home in your hearts as you trust in him. Your roots will grow down into God's love and keep you strong. And may you have the power to understand, as all God's people should, how wide, how long, how high, and how deep his love is. May you experience the love of Christ, though it is too great to understand fully. Then you will be made complete with all the fullness of life and power that comes from God. (Eph. 3:16–19 NLT)

> His divine power has given us everything we need for a godly life through our knowledge of him who called us by his own glory and goodness. (2 Pet. 1:3 NIV)

Tidbits & Morsels: Surely, God has empowered you to say no to a baker offering you a donut hole, a deli worker a slice of cheese, and a bank teller a lollipop.

____

____

____

Encouragement

> Unrelenting disappointment leaves you heartsick, but a sudden good break can turn life around. (Prov. 13:12 MSG)

> So let's agree to use all our energy in getting along with each other. Help others with encouraging words; don't drag them down by finding fault. You're certainly not going to permit an argument over what is served or not served at supper to wreck God's work among you, are you? I said it before and I'll say it again: All food is good, but it can turn bad if you use it badly, if you use it to trip others up and send them sprawling. (Rom. 14:19–20 MSG)

> Let everything you say be good and helpful, so that your words will be an encouragement to those who hear them. (Eph. 4:29 NLT)

> Let the message of Christ dwell among you richly as you teach and admonish one another with all wisdom through psalms, hymns, and songs from the Spirit, singing to God with gratitude in your hearts. (Col. 3:16 NIV)

> Therefore encourage one another and build each other up, just as in fact you are doing. (1 Thess. 5:11 NIV)

> And let us consider one another in order to stir up love and good works, not forsaking the assembling of ourselves together, as is the manner of some, but exhorting one another, and so much the more as you see the Day approaching. (Heb. 10:24–25 NKJV)

Tidbits & Morsels: Today, thank someone who's had a positive impact on your life, then pay it forward.

____

____

____

Envy & Jealousy

Do not worship any other god, for the Lord, whose name is Jealous, is a jealous God. (Ex. 34:14 NIV)

But as for me, I almost lost my footing. My feet were slipping, and I was almost gone. For I envied the proud when I saw them prosper despite their wickedness. (Ps. 73:2–3 NLT)

A heart at peace gives life to the body, but envy rots the bones. (Prov. 14:30 NIV)

Wrath is cruel, anger is overwhelming, but who can stand before jealousy? (Prov. 27:4 ESV)

Then I observed that the basic motive for success is the driving force of envy and jealousy! But this, too, is foolishness, chasing the wind. (Eccl. 4:4 TLB)

For where jealousy and selfish ambition exist, there will be disorder and every vile practice. But the wisdom from above is first pure, then peaceable, gentle, open to reason, full of mercy and good fruits, impartial and sincere. And a harvest of righteousness is sown in peace by those who make peace. (James 3:16–18 ESV)

Tidbits & Morsels: Write down three good qualities about that friend who eats anything she wants and never gains weight—then tell her what you wrote.

____

____

____

Evil One or Satan

The serpent was clever, more clever than any wild animal God had made. He spoke to the Woman: "Do

I understand that God told you not to eat from any tree in the garden?" The Woman said to the serpent, "Not at all. We can eat from the trees in the garden. It's only about the tree in the middle of the garden that God said, 'Don't eat from it; don't even touch it or you'll die.'" The serpent told the Woman, "You won't die. God knows that the moment you eat from that tree, you'll see what's really going on. You'll be just like God, knowing everything, ranging all the way from good to evil." (Gen. 3:1–5 MSG)

[Jesus] But turning and seeing his disciples, he rebuked Peter and said, "Get behind me, Satan! For you are not setting your mind on the things of God, but on the things of man." (Mark 8:33 ESV)

[Jesus] The thief comes only to steal and kill and destroy. I came that they may have life and have it abundantly. (John 10:10 ESV)

Even Satan disguises himself as an angel of light. (2 Cor. 11:14 NLT)

Be sober-minded; be watchful. Your adversary the devil prowls around like a roaring lion, seeking someone to devour. Resist him, firm in your faith, knowing that the same kinds of suffering are being experienced by your brotherhood throughout the world. (1 Pet. 5:8–9 ESV)

Tidbits & Morsels: While you can underestimate the power of Satan, you can never overestimate the power of God!

____

____

____

Examine Your Ways (Take Inventory)

God made my life complete when I placed all the pieces before him. When I cleaned up my act, he gave me a fresh start. Indeed, I've kept alert to GOD's ways; I haven't taken God for granted. Every day I review the ways he works, I try not to miss a trick. I feel put back together, and I'm watching my step. GOD rewrote the text of my life when I opened the book of my heart to his eyes. (2 Sam. 22:21–25 MSG)

When I think on my ways, I turn my feet to your testimonies; I hasten and do not delay to keep your commandments. (Ps. 119:59–60 ESV)

Let us test and examine our ways, and return to the LORD! (Lam. 3:40 ESV)

"Think it over," says the Lord Almighty. "Consider how you have acted and what has happened as a result!" (Hag. 1:7 TLB)

Check up on yourselves. Are you really Christians? Do you pass the test? Do you feel Christ's presence and power more and more within you? Or are you just pretending to be Christians when actually you aren't at all? (2 Cor. 13:5 TLB)

Tidbits & Morsels: Examine (and record) the reasons for your good behavior and the excuses for your bad behavior.

____

____

____

EXCUSES & RATIONALIZATION

The more talk, the less truth; the wise measure their words. (Prov. 10:19 MSG)

[Jesus] If I had not come and spoken to them, they would not have been guilty of sin, but now they have no excuse for their sin. (John 15:22 ESV)

Obviously, the law applies to those to whom it was given, for its purpose is to keep people from having excuses, and to show that the entire world is guilty before God. (Rom. 3:19 NLT)

Don't be fooled by those who try to excuse these sins, for the terrible wrath of God is upon all those who do them. Don't even associate with such people. For though once your heart was full of darkness, now it is full of light from the Lord, and your behavior should show it! (Eph. 5:6–8 TLB)

It is God's will that your honorable lives should silence those ignorant people who make foolish accusations against you. For you are free, yet you are God's slaves, so don't use your freedom as an excuse to do evil. (1 Pet. 2:15–16 NLT)

Tidbits & Morsels: Don't look for a loophole; look for a foothold.

____

____

____

Exhaustion & Weariness

The man declares, I am weary, O God; I am weary, O God, and worn out. Surely I am too stupid to be a man. I have not the understanding of a man. I have not learned wisdom, nor have I knowledge of the Holy One. (Prov. 30:1–3 ESV)

Have you not known? Have you not heard? The Lord is the everlasting God, the Creator of the ends of the earth. He does not faint or grow weary; his understanding is unsearchable. He gives power to the faint, and to him who has no might he increases strength. Even youths shall faint and be weary, and young men shall fall exhausted; but they who wait for the LORD shall renew their strength; they shall mount up with wings like eagles; they shall run and not be weary; they shall walk and not faint. (Isa. 40:28–31 ESV)

"For I [the LORD] will satisfy the weary soul, and every languishing soul I will replenish." At this I awoke and looked, and my sleep was pleasant to me. (Jer. 31:25–26 ESV)

[Jesus] Are you tired? Worn out? Burned out on religion? Come to me. Get away with me and you'll recover your life. I'll show you how to take a real rest. Walk with me and work with me—watch how I do it. Learn the unforced rhythms of grace. I won't lay anything heavy or ill-fitting on you. Keep company with me and you'll learn to live freely and lightly. (Matt. 11:28–30 MSG)

We are pressed on every side by troubles, but not crushed and broken. We are perplexed because we don't know why things happen as they do, but we don't give up and quit. We are hunted down, but God never abandons us. We get knocked down, but we get up again and keep going. These bodies of ours are constantly facing death just as Jesus did; so it is clear to all that it is only the living Christ within who keeps us safe. (2 Cor. 4:8–10 TLB)

Tidbits & Morsels: Emotional turmoil is one of the main causes of physical exhaustion.

____

____

____

Fad Diets & Legalistic Eating

[Jesus] Then are you also without understanding? Do you not see that whatever goes into a person from outside cannot defile him, since it enters not his heart but his stomach, and is expelled? (Thus he declared all foods clean.) (Mark 7:18–19 ESV)

But Peter explained it to them in order from the beginning, saying: "I was in the city of Joppa praying; and in a trance I saw a vision, an object descending like a great sheet, let down from heaven by four corners; and it came to me. When I observed it intently and considered, I saw four-footed animals of the earth, wild beasts, creeping things, and birds of the air. And I heard a voice saying to me, 'Rise, Peter; kill and eat.' But I said, 'Not so, Lord! For nothing common or unclean has at any time entered my mouth.' But the voice answered me again from heaven, 'What God has cleansed you must not call common.' Now this was done three times, and all were drawn up again into heaven." (Acts 11:4–10 NKJV)

Some are accustomed to thinking of idols as being real, so when they eat food that has been offered to idols, they think of it as the worship of real gods, and their weak consciences are violated. It's true that we can't win God's approval by what we eat. We don't lose anything if we don't eat it, and we don't gain anything if we do. But you must be careful so that your freedom does not cause others with a weaker conscience to stumble. (1 Cor. 8:7–9 NLT)

Since you died with Christ to the elemental spiritual forces of this world, why, as though you still belonged to the world, do you submit to its rules: "Do not handle! Do not taste! Do not touch!"? These rules, which have to do with things that are all destined to perish with use, are based on merely human commands and teachings. Such regulations indeed have an appearance of wisdom, with their self-imposed worship, their false humility, and their harsh treatment of the body, but they lack any value in restraining sensual indulgence. (Col. 2:20–23 NIV)

For everything created by God is good, and nothing is to be rejected if it is received with thanksgiving, for it is made holy by the word of God and prayer. (1 Tim. 4:4–5 ESV)

Tidbits & Morsels: Don't waste a perfectly good appetite on food you don't enjoy.

Faith & Faithfulness

Yet this is what the Sovereign Lord says: ... "If you do not stand firm in your faith, you will not stand at all." (Isa. 7:7, 9 NIV)

[Jesus] Truly, I say to you, if you have faith and do not doubt, you will not only do what has been done to the fig tree, but even if you say to this mountain, "Be taken up and thrown into the sea," it will happen. And whatever you ask in prayer, you will receive, if you have faith. (Matt. 21:21–22 ESV)

So faith comes from hearing, that is, hearing the Good News about Christ. (Rom. 10:17 NLT)

So we are always of good courage. We know that while we are at home in the body we are away from the Lord, for we walk by faith, not by sight. (2 Cor. 5:6–7 ESV)

Now before faith came, we were held captive under the law, imprisoned until the coming faith would be revealed. So then, the law was our guardian until Christ came, in order that we might be justified by faith. But now that faith has come, we are no longer under a guardian, for in Christ Jesus you are all sons of God, through faith. (Gal. 3:23–26 ESV)

> Now faith is the assurance of things hoped for, the conviction of things not seen. ... And without faith it is impossible to please him, for whoever would draw near to God must believe that he exists and that he rewards those who seek him. (Heb. 11:1, 6 ESV)

> Now someone may argue, "Some people have faith; others have good deeds." But I say, "How can you show me your faith if you don't have good deeds? I will show you my faith by my good deeds." You say you have faith, for you believe that there is one God. Good for you! Even the demons believe this, and they tremble in terror. How foolish! Can't you see that faith without good deeds is useless? (James 2:18–20 NLT)

Tidbits & Morsels: To increase your faith, feed on God's Word, pray, and worship with fellow believers. Good deeds will show proof of your faith.

____

____

____

FALSE TEACHERS

> Swindlers and scoundrels talk out of both sides of their mouths. They wink at each other, they shuffle their feet, they cross their fingers behind their backs. Their perverse minds are always cooking up something nasty, always stirring up trouble. (Prov. 6:12–14 MSG)

> [Jesus] Beware of false prophets, who come to you in sheep's clothing but inwardly are ravenous wolves. You will recognize them by their fruits. Are grapes gathered from thornbushes, or figs from thistles? (Matt. 7:15–16 ESV)

Now I urge you, brethren, note those who cause divisions and offenses, contrary to the doctrine which you learned, and avoid them. For those who are such do not serve our Lord Jesus Christ, but their own belly, and by smooth words and flattering speech deceive the hearts of the simple. (Rom. 16:17–18 NKJV)

The Spirit makes it clear that as time goes on, some are going to give up on the faith and chase after demonic illusions put forth by professional liars. These liars have lied so well and for so long that they've lost their capacity for truth. They will tell you not to get married. They'll tell you not to eat this or that food—perfectly good food God created to be eaten heartily and with thanksgiving by believers who know better! Everything God created is good, and to be received with thanks. Nothing is to be sneered at and thrown out. God's Word and our prayers make every item in creation holy. (1 Tim. 4:1–5 MSG)

Jesus Christ is the same yesterday, today, and forever. So do not be attracted by strange, new ideas. Your spiritual strength comes as a gift from God, not from ceremonial rules about eating certain foods—a method which, by the way, hasn't helped those who have tried it! (Heb. 13:8–9 TLB)

Tidbits & Morsels: Put your confidence in God, not in a misguided diet guru puffed up with pride.

____

____

____

Fasting

Mordecai sent her [Esther] this message: "Don't think that just because you live in the king's house you're the

> one Jew who will get out of this alive. If you persist in staying silent at a time like this, help and deliverance will arrive for the Jews from someplace else; but you and your family will be wiped out. Who knows? Maybe you were made queen for just such a time as this." Esther sent back her answer to Mordecai: "Go and get all the Jews living in Susa together. Fast for me. Don't eat or drink for three days, either day or night. I and my maids will fast with you. If you will do this, I'll go to the king, even though it's forbidden. If I die, I die." (Est. 4:12–16 MSG)

> No, this is the kind of fasting I want: Free those who are wrongly imprisoned; lighten the burden of those who work for you. Let the oppressed go free, and remove the chains that bind people. Share your food with the hungry, and give shelter to the homeless. Give clothes to those who need them, and do not hide from relatives who need your help. (Isa. 58:6–7 NLT)

> [Jesus] And after fasting forty days and forty nights, he [Jesus] was hungry. And the tempter came and said to him, "If you are the Son of God, command these stones to become loaves of bread." But he answered, "It is written, 'Man shall not live by bread alone, but by every word that comes from the mouth of God.'" (Matt. 4:2–4 ESV)

> [Jesus] And now about fasting. When you fast, declining your food for a spiritual purpose, don't do it publicly, as the hypocrites do, who try to look wan and disheveled so people will feel sorry for them. Truly, that is the only reward they will ever get. But when you fast, put on festive clothing, so that no one will suspect you are hungry, except your Father who knows every secret. And he will reward you. (Matt. 6:16–18 TLB)

Tidbits & Morsels: Push your hunger aside long enough to pray for those whose cupboards are bare.

Fear & Insecurity

It is the LORD who goes before you. He will be with you; he will not leave you or forsake you. Do not fear or be dismayed. (Deut. 31:8 ESV)

God is our refuge and strength, an ever-present help in trouble. Therefore we will not fear, though the earth give way and the mountains fall into the heart of the sea, though its waters roar and foam and the mountains quake with their surging. (Ps. 46:1–3 NIV)

In my distress I prayed to the LORD, and the LORD answered me and set me free. The Lord is for me, so I will have no fear. What can mere people do to me? (Ps. 118:5-6 NLT)

Don't panic. I'm with you. There's no need to fear for I'm your God. I'll give you strength. I'll help you. I'll hold you steady, keep a firm grip on you. (Isa. 41:10 MSG)

We need have no fear of someone who loves us perfectly; his [God's] perfect love for us eliminates all dread of what he might do to us. If we are afraid, it is for fear of what he might do to us and shows that we are not fully convinced that he really loves us. (1 John 4:18 TLB)

Tidbits & Morsels: Take a deep breath, then whisper this prayer, "In Jesus's name, I will not fear."

Fear of Failure or Success

> It is pleasant to see dreams come true, but fools refuse to turn from evil to attain them. (Prov. 13:19 NLT)

> For I, the Lord your God, hold your right hand; it is I who say to you, "Fear not, I am the one who helps you." (Isa. 41:13 ESV)

> When life is heavy and hard to take, go off by yourself. Enter the silence. Bow in prayer. Don't ask questions: Wait for hope to appear. Don't run from trouble. Take it full-face. The "worst" is never the worst. (Lam. 3:28–30 MSG)

> And we know that God causes everything to work together for the good of those who love God and are called according to his purpose for them. (Rom. 8:28 NLT)

> So if you're serious about living this new resurrection life with Christ, act like it. Pursue the things over which Christ presides. Don't shuffle along, eyes to the ground, absorbed with the things right in front of you. Look up and be alert to what is going on around Christ—that's where the action is. See things from his perspective. (Col. 3:1–2 MSG)

> For this reason I remind you to fan into flame the gift of God, which is in you through the laying on of my hands, for God gave us a spirit not of fear but of power and love and self-control. (2 Tim. 1:6–7 ESV)

Tidbits & Morsels: What is the worst thing that could happen if you fail or succeed? You can either start over or keep going. There is no standing still.

___

___

___

Focus

Let your eyes look straight ahead; fix your gaze directly before you. Give careful thought to the paths for your feet and be steadfast in all your ways. Do not turn to the right or the left; keep your foot from evil. (Prov. 4:25–27 NIV)

For the Lord God will help Me; therefore I will not be disgraced; therefore I have set My face like a flint, and I know that I will not be ashamed. (Isa. 50:7 NKJV)

[Jesus] Here's what I want you to do: Find a quiet, secluded place so you won't be tempted to role-play before God. Just be there as simply and honestly as you can manage. The focus will shift from you to God, and you will begin to sense his grace. (Matt. 6:6 MSG)

Focusing on the self is the opposite of focusing on God. Anyone completely absorbed in self ignores God, ends up thinking more about self than God. That person ignores who God is and what he is doing. And God isn't pleased at being ignored. (Rom. 8:7–8 MSG)

Fix your thoughts on what is true, and honorable, and right, and pure, and lovely, and admirable. Think about things that are excellent and worthy of praise. (Phil. 4:8 NLT)

Tidbits & Morsels: Do not work or play while you eat your meals. Focus on the food and the fellowship with which God has blessed you.

___

___

___

Food Choices

And God said, "Behold, I have given you every plant yielding seed that is on the face of all the earth, and every tree with seed in its fruit. You shall have them for food." (Gen. 1:29 ESV)

Every moving thing that lives shall be food for you. And as I gave you the green plants, I give you everything. (Gen. 9:3 ESV)

If my people would only listen to me, if Israel would only follow my ways, how quickly I would subdue their enemies and turn my hand against their foes! Those who hate the Lord would cringe before him, and their punishment would last forever. But you would be fed with the finest of wheat; with honey from the rock I would satisfy you. (Ps. 81:13–16 NIV)

The tender grass grows up at his command to feed the cattle, and there are fruit trees, vegetables, and grain for man to cultivate, and wine to make him glad, and olive oil as lotion for his skin, and bread to give him strength. (Ps. 104:14–15 TLB)

On this mountain the Lord Almighty will prepare a feast of rich food for all peoples, a banquet of aged wine— the best of meats and the finest of wines. (Isa. 25:6 NIV)

Now the Holy Spirit tells us clearly that in the last times some will turn away from the true faith; they will follow deceptive spirits and teachings that come from demons. These people are hypocrites and liars, and their consciences are dead. They will say it is wrong to be married and wrong to eat certain foods. But God created those foods to be eaten with thanks by faithful people who know the truth. Since everything God created is good, we should not reject any of it but receive it with thanks. For we know it is made acceptable by the word of God and prayer. (1 Tim. 4:1–5 NLT)

Tidbits & Morsels: We are free to choose from God's bounty! Choose wisely.

___

___

___

Forgiveness & Making Amends

He [the Lord] will not always chide, nor will he keep his anger forever. He does not deal with us according to our sins, nor repay us according to our iniquities. For as high as the heavens are above the earth, so great is his steadfast love toward those who fear him; as far as the east is from the west, so far does he remove our transgressions from us. (Ps. 103:9–12 ESV)

[Jesus] So if you are offering your gift at the altar and there remember that your brother has something against you, leave your gift there before the altar and go. First be reconciled to your brother, and then come and offer your gift. (Matt. 5:23–24 ESV)

[Jesus] For if you forgive others their trespasses, your heavenly Father will also forgive you, but if you do not forgive others their trespasses, neither will your Father forgive your trespasses. (Matt. 6:14–15 ESV)

[Jesus] Then Peter came to him and asked, "Sir, how often should I forgive a brother who sins against me? Seven times?" "No!" Jesus replied, "Seventy times seven!" (Matt. 18:21–22 TLB)

[Jesus, speaking of immoral woman who washed his feet with her tears]: I tell you, her sins—and they are many—have been forgiven, so she has shown me much love. But a person who is forgiven little shows only little love. (Luke 7:47 NLT)

[Jesus] If you forgive someone's sins, they're gone for good. If you don't forgive sins, what are you going to do with them? (John 20:23 MSG)

Put on then, as God's chosen ones, holy and beloved, compassionate hearts, kindness, humility, meekness, and patience, bearing with one another and, if one has a complaint against another, forgiving each other; as the Lord has forgiven you, so you also must forgive. And above all these put on love, which binds everything together in perfect harmony. (Col. 3:12–14 ESV)

Tidbits & Morsels: Unforgiveness will eat at you until you eat over it. Offer forgiveness to someone today—whether they accept it or not.

____

____

____

Freedom vs. Legalism

I am the Lord your God, who brought you out of the land of Egypt so you would no longer be their slaves. I broke the yoke of slavery from your neck so you can walk with your heads held high. (Lev. 26:13 NLT)

I will walk in freedom, for I have devoted myself to your commandments. (Ps. 119:45 NLT)

The Spirit of the Lord God is upon Me, because the Lord has anointed Me to preach good tidings to the poor; He has sent Me to heal the brokenhearted, to proclaim liberty to the captives, and the opening of the prison to those who are bound; to proclaim the acceptable year of the Lord, and the day of vengeance of our God; to comfort all who mourn, to console those who mourn in Zion, to give them beauty for ashes, the oil of joy for mourning, the garment of praise for the spirit of heaviness; that they may be called trees of righteousness, the planting of the LORD, that He may be glorified. (Isa. 61:1–3 NKJV)

Likewise, my brothers, you also have died to the law through the body of Christ, so that you may belong to another, to him who has been raised from the dead, in order that we may bear fruit for God. For while we were living in the flesh, our sinful passions, aroused by the law, were at work in our members to bear fruit for death. But now we are released from the law, having died to that which held us captive, so that we serve in the new way of the Spirit and not in the old way of the written code. (Rom. 7:4–6 ESV)

O foolish Galatians! Who has bewitched you that you should not obey the truth, before whose eyes Jesus Christ was clearly portrayed among you as crucified? This only I want to learn from you: Did you receive the Spirit by the works of the law, or by the hearing of faith? Are you so foolish? Having begun in the Spirit, are you now being made perfect by the flesh? Have you suffered so many things in vain—if indeed it was in vain? Therefore He who supplies the Spirit to you and works miracles among you, does He do it by the works of the law, or by the hearing of faith?—just as Abraham "believed God, and it was accounted to him for righteousness." (Gal. 3:1–6 NKJV)

It is for freedom that Christ has set us free. Stand firm, then, and do not let yourselves be burdened again by a yoke of slavery. ... You, my brothers and sisters, were called to be free. But do not use your freedom to indulge the flesh; rather, serve one another humbly in love. (Gal. 5:1, 13 NIV)

Don't let anyone capture you with empty philosophies and high-sounding nonsense that come from human thinking and from the spiritual powers of this world, rather than from Christ. (Col. 2:8 NLT)

Tidbits & Morsels: Occasionally, allow yourself a planned treat. Let freedom ring!

____

____

____

Friendships & Relationships

The friendship of the LORD is for those who fear him, and he makes known to them his covenant. (Ps. 25:14 ESV)

Overlook an offense and bond a friendship; fasten on to a slight and—good-bye, friend! ... Friends love through all kinds of weather, and families stick together in all kinds of trouble. (Prov. 17:9, 17 MSG)

Friends come and friends go, but a true friend sticks by you like family. (Prov. 18:24 MSG)

Make no friendship with a man given to anger, nor go with a wrathful man, lest you learn his ways and entangle yourself in a snare. (Prov. 22:24–25 ESV)

Oil and perfume make the heart glad, and the sweetness of a friend comes from his earnest counsel. (Prov. 27:9 ESV)

Greater love has no one than this, than to lay down one's life for his friends. (John 15:13 NKJV)

Don't be too proud to enjoy the company of ordinary people. And don't think you know it all! (Rom. 12:16 NLT)

Do not be yoked together with unbelievers. For what do righteousness and wickedness have in common? Or what fellowship can light have with darkness? (2 Cor. 6:14 NIV)

> You adulterous people! Do you not know that friendship with the world is enmity with God? Therefore whoever wishes to be a friend of the world makes himself an enemy of God. (James 4:4 ESV)

Tidbits & Morsels: Friends influence one another—for good or bad, for love or hate, for peace or angst, for faith or doubt, or for food or fast. What kind of influencer are you?

___

___

___

Frustration

> There was a time when I wouldn't admit what a sinner I was. But my dishonesty made me miserable and filled my days with frustration. (Ps. 32:3 TLB)

> The desires of good people lead straight to the best, but wicked ambition ends in angry frustration. (Prov. 11:23 MSG)

> A rebel's frustrations are heavier than sand and rocks. (Prov. 27:3 TLB)

> We can rejoice, too, when we run into problems and trials, for we know that they help us develop endurance. And endurance develops strength of character, and character strengthens our confident hope of salvation. And this hope will not lead to disappointment. For we know how dearly God loves us, because he has given us the Holy Spirit to fill our hearts with his love. (Rom. 5:3–5 NLT)

Tidbits & Morsels: Women, don't get frustrated when the men in your life lose weight faster than you do. Instead, be thankful you don't have their body hair.

____

____

____

Give God Credit & Glory

I give you all the credit, God—you got me out of that mess, you didn't let my foes gloat. (Ps. 30:1 MSG)

With all my heart I will praise you, O Lord my God. I will give glory to your name forever. (Ps. 86:12 NLT)

Not to us, O Lord, not to us, but to your name give glory, for the sake of your steadfast love and your faithfulness! (Ps. 115:1 ESV)

So whether you eat or drink or whatever you do, do it all for the glory of God. Do not cause anyone to stumble, whether Jews, Greeks or the church of God—even as I try to please everyone in every way. For I am not seeking my own good but the good of many, so that they may be saved. (1 Cor. 10:31–33 NIV)

Now to him who is able to keep you from stumbling and to present you blameless before the presence of his glory with great joy, to the only God, our Savior, through Jesus Christ our Lord, be glory, majesty, dominion, and authority, before all time and now and forever. Amen. (Jude 24–25 ESV)

O Lord, you are worthy to receive the glory and the honor and the power, for you have created all things. They were created and called into being by your act of will. (Rev. 4:11 TLB)

Tidbits & Morsels: If you give God the glory for your success, he may bless you with more success.

____

____

____

GLOAT

Do not rejoice when your enemy falls, and let not your heart be glad when he stumbles, lest the LORD see it and be displeased, and turn away his anger from him. (Prov. 24:17–18 ESV)

You shouldn't have gloated over your brother when he was down-and-out. You shouldn't have laughed and joked at Judah's sons when they were facedown in the mud. You shouldn't have talked so big when everything was so bad. You shouldn't have taken advantage of my people when their lives had fallen apart. (Obad. 1:12–13 MSG)

Don't, enemy, crow over me. I'm down, but I'm not out. I'm sitting in the dark right now, but GOD is my light. I can take GOD's punishing rage. I deserve it—I sinned. But it's not forever. He's on my side and is going to get me out of this. He'll turn on the lights and show me his ways. I'll see the whole picture and how right he is. And my enemy will see it, too, and be discredited—yes, disgraced! This enemy who kept taunting, "So where is this GOD of yours?" I'm going to see it with these, my own eyes— my enemy disgraced, trash in the gutter. (Mic. 7:8–10 MSG)

Behind and underneath all this there is a holy, God-planted, God-tended root. If the primary root of the tree is holy, there's bound to be some holy fruit. Some of the tree's branches were pruned and you wild olive shoots were grafted in. Yet the fact that you are now fed by that rich and holy root gives you no cause to gloat over the pruned branches. Remember, you aren't feeding the root; the root is feeding you. (Rom. 11:16–18 MSG)

Tidbits & Morsels: Gloating may be the opposite of sulking, but both behaviors are equally unattractive.

Gluttony & Overeating

> The good man eats to live, while the evil man lives to eat. (Prov. 13:25 TLB)
>
> The wise store up choice food and olive oil, but fools gulp theirs down. (Prov. 21:20 NIV)
>
> When you sit down to eat with a ruler, observe carefully what is before you, and put a knife to your throat if you are given to appetite. Do not desire his delicacies, for they are deceptive food. (Prov. 23:1–3 ESV)
>
> When you're given a box of candy, don't gulp it all down; eat too much chocolate and you'll make yourself sick. (Prov. 25:16 MSG)
>
> Do you not know that you are the temple of God and that the Spirit of God dwells in you? If anyone defiles the temple of God, God will destroy him. For the temple of God is holy, which temple you are. (1 Cor. 3:16–17 NKJV)
>
> For many, of whom I have often told you and now tell you even with tears, walk as enemies of the cross of Christ. Their end is destruction, their god is their belly, and they glory in their shame, with minds set on earthly things. (Phil. 3:18–19 ESV)

Tidbits & Morsels: Overeating will not untie that knot in your stomach; overeating will double and tighten the knot.

GOOD EXAMPLE OR WITNESS

[Jesus] You are the light of the world. A city set on a hill cannot be hidden. Nor do people light a lamp and put it under a basket, but on a stand, and it gives light to all in the house. In the same way, let your light shine before others, so that they may see your good works and give glory to your Father who is in heaven. (Matt. 5:14–16 ESV)

Always be full of joy in the Lord; I say it again, rejoice! Let everyone see that you are unselfish and considerate in all you do. (Phil. 4:4–5 TLB)

And here you yourself must be an example to them of good deeds of every kind. Let everything you do reflect your love of the truth and the fact that you are in dead earnest about it. Your conversation should be so sensible and logical that anyone who wants to argue will be ashamed of himself because there won't be anything to criticize in anything you say! (Titus 2:7–8 TLB)

And I pray that as you share your faith with others it will grip their lives too, as they see the wealth of good things in you that come from Christ Jesus. (Philem. 6 TLB)

Live such good lives among the pagans that, though they accuse you of doing wrong, they may see your good deeds and glorify God on the day he visits us. (1 Pet. 2:12 NIV)

Who is going to harm you if you are eager to do good? But even if you should suffer for what is right, you are blessed. "Do not fear their threats; do not be frightened." But in your hearts revere Christ as Lord. Always be prepared to give an answer to everyone who asks you to give the reason for the hope that you have. But do this with gentleness and respect, keeping a clear conscience, so that those who speak maliciously against your good behavior in Christ may be ashamed of their slander. (1 Pet. 3:13–16 NIV)

Tidbits & Morsels: Does your life story tell of God's goodness, or is your story a cautionary tale? Either way, God will use them both.

____

____

____

Good Health

It was there at Marah that the Lord laid before them the following conditions, to test their commitment to him: "If you will listen to the voice of the Lord your God, and obey it, and do what is right, then I will not make you suffer the diseases I sent on the Egyptians, for I am the Lord who heals you." (Ex. 15:25–26 TLB

O Lord my God, I pleaded with you, and you gave me my health again. (Ps. 30:2 TLB)

A cheerful disposition is good for your health; gloom and doom leave you bone-tired. (Prov. 17:22 MSG)

So refuse to worry, and keep your body healthy. (Eccl. 11:10 NLT)

The Lord will guide you continually, giving you water when you are dry and restoring your strength. You will be like a well-watered garden, like an ever-flowing spring. (Isa. 58:11 NLT)

Are you hurting? Pray. Do you feel great? Sing. Are you sick? Call the church leaders together to pray and anoint you with oil in the name of the Master. Believing-prayer will heal you, and Jesus will put you on your feet. And if you've sinned, you'll be forgiven—healed inside and out. (James 5:14–15 MSG)

Beloved, I pray that all may go well with you and that you may be in good health, as it goes well with your soul. (3 John 2 ESV)

Tidbits & Morsels: Don't cancel your yearly physical because you dread getting on the doctor's scale. (Oh, come on, you know you've done that.)

____

____

____

Grace

What shall we say then? Are we to continue in sin that grace may abound? By no means! How can we who died to sin still live in it? Do you not know that all of us who have been baptized into Christ Jesus were baptized into his death? We were buried therefore with him by baptism into death, in order that, just as Christ was raised from the dead by the glory of the Father, we too might walk in newness of life. (Rom. 6:1–4 ESV)

As God's co-workers we urge you not to receive God's grace in vain. For he says, "In the time of my favor I heard you, and in the day of salvation I helped you." I tell you, now is the time of God's favor, now is the day of salvation. (2 Cor. 6:1–2 NIV)

> But God is so rich in mercy, and he loved us so much, that even though we were dead because of our sins, he gave us life when he raised Christ from the dead. (It is only by God's grace that you have been saved!) ... God saved you by his grace when you believed. And you can't take credit for this; it is a gift from God. Salvation is not a reward for the good things we have done, so none of us can boast about it. For we are God's masterpiece. He has created us anew in Christ Jesus, so we can do the good things he planned for us long ago. (Eph. 2:4–5, 8–10 NLT)

> For the grace of God has appeared, bringing salvation for all people, training us to renounce ungodliness and worldly passions, and to live self-controlled, upright, and godly lives in the present age. (Titus 2:11–12 ESV)

> Let us then with confidence draw near to the throne of grace, that we may receive mercy and find grace to help in time of need. (Heb. 4:16 ESV)

> But now I find that I must write about something else, urging you to defend the faith that God has entrusted once for all time to his holy people. I say this because some ungodly people have wormed their way into your churches, saying that God's marvelous grace allows us to live immoral lives. The condemnation of such people was recorded long ago, for they have denied our only Master and Lord, Jesus Christ. (Jude 3–4 NLT)

Tidbits & Morsels: God gives you the grace to accomplish all that he calls you to do.

____

____

____

Greed & Self-indulgence

A freeloader has twin daughters named "Gimme" and "Gimme more." (Prov. 30:15 MSG)

My people come to you, as they usually do, and sit before you to hear your words, but they do not put them into practice. Their mouths speak of love, but their hearts are greedy for unjust gain. (Ezek. 33:31 NIV)

[Jesus] Woe to you, scribes and Pharisees, hypocrites! For you clean the outside of the cup and the plate, but inside they are full of greed and self-indulgence. You blind Pharisee! First clean the inside of the cup and the plate, that the outside also may be clean. (Matt. 23:25–26 ESV)

Put to death, therefore, whatever belongs to your earthly nature: sexual immorality, impurity, lust, evil desires and greed, which is idolatry. (Col. 3:5 NIV)

You have lived on the earth in luxury and in self-indulgence. You have fattened your hearts in a day of slaughter. (James 5:5 ESV)

Tidbits & Morsels: List all the costly fad diets you have followed which ended in permanent weight loss. (Yeah, I thought so.)

___

___

___

Guilt

Because of your wrath there is no health in my body; there is no soundness in my bones because of my sin. My guilt has overwhelmed me like a burden too heavy to bear. (Ps. 38:3–4 NIV)

> O God, you know my folly; the wrongs I have done are not hidden from you. (Ps. 69:5 ESV)

> Fools make fun of guilt, but the godly acknowledge it and seek reconciliation. (Prov. 14:9 NLT)

> The way of the guilty is crooked, but the conduct of the pure is upright. (Prov. 21:8 ESV)

> The wicked are edgy with guilt, ready to run off even when no one's after them; honest people are relaxed and confident, bold as lions. (Prov. 28:1 MSG)

> And since we have a great High Priest who rules over God's house, let us go right into the presence of God with sincere hearts fully trusting him. For our guilty consciences have been sprinkled with Christ's blood to make us clean, and our bodies have been washed with pure water. (Heb. 10:21–22 NLT)

Tidbits & Morsels: Don't let others make you feel guilty about what you eat. When and what you eat is between you and God.

____

____

____

GULLIBLE

> The simple believe anything, but the prudent give thought to their steps. (Prov. 14:15 NIV)

> And so while there has never been any question about your honesty in these matters—I couldn't be more proud of you!—I want you also to be smart, making sure every "good" thing is the real thing. Don't be gullible in regard to smooth-talking evil. Stay alert like this, and before you know it the God of peace will come down on Satan with both feet, stomping him into the dirt. Enjoy the best of Jesus! (Rom. 16:19–20 MSG)

I am anxious for you with the deep concern of God himself—anxious that your love should be for Christ alone, just as a pure maiden saves her love for one man only, for the one who will be her husband. But I am frightened, fearing that in some way you will be led away from your pure and simple devotion to our Lord, just as Eve was deceived by Satan in the Garden of Eden. You seem so gullible: you believe whatever anyone tells you even if he is preaching about another Jesus than the one we preach, or a different spirit than the Holy Spirit you received, or shows you a different way to be saved. You swallow it all. (2 Cor. 11:2–4 TLB)

My dear friends, don't believe everything you hear. Carefully weigh and examine what people tell you. Not everyone who talks about God comes from God. There are a lot of lying preachers loose in the world. (1 John 4:1 MSG)

Tidbits & Morsels: Don't be flimflammed by all those diet commercials promising miracles. Please, don't.

____

____

____

Heart

Create in me a clean heart, O God, and renew a right spirit within me. Cast me not away from your presence, and take not your Holy Spirit from me. Restore to me the joy of your salvation, and uphold me with a willing spirit. Then I will teach transgressors your ways, and sinners will return to you. (Ps. 51:10–13 ESV)

Search me, O God, and know my heart; test my thoughts. Point out anything you find in me that makes you sad and lead me along the path of everlasting life. (Ps. 139:23–24 TLB)

> Above all else, guard your heart, for everything you do flows from it. (Prov. 4:23 NIV)

> Blessed is the one who always trembles before God, but whoever hardens their heart falls into trouble. (Prov. 28:14 NIV)

> The heart is hopelessly dark and deceitful, a puzzle that no one can figure out. But I, God, search the heart and examine the mind. I get to the heart of the human. I get to the root of things. I treat them as they really are, not as they pretend to be. (Jer. 17:9–10 MSG)

> And I will give you a new heart, and a new spirit I will put within you. And I will remove the heart of stone from your flesh and give you a heart of flesh. (Ezek. 36:26 ESV)

> [Jesus] The good person out of the good treasure of his heart produces good, and the evil person out of his evil treasure produces evil, for out of the abundance of the heart his mouth speaks. (Luke 6:45 ESV)

Tidbits & Morsels: Stop right now and search your heart, then record both the beautiful and the ugly.

____

____

____

Hit Rock Bottom

> Be gracious to me, O Lord, for I am in distress; my eye is wasted from grief; my soul and my body also. For my life is spent with sorrow, and my years with sighing; my strength fails because of my iniquity, and my bones waste away. (Ps. 31:9–10 ESV)

> Lord, you are the God who saves me; day and night I cry out to you. May my prayer come before you; turn

your ear to my cry. I am overwhelmed with troubles and my life draws near to death. I am counted among those who go down to the pit; I am like one without strength. (Ps. 88:1–4 NIV)

Help, GOD—I've hit rock bottom! Master, hear my cry for help! Listen hard! Open your ears! Listen to my cries for mercy. (Ps. 130:1–2 MSG)

Answer me speedily, O LORD; my spirit fails! Do not hide Your face from me, lest I be like those who go down into the pit. Cause me to hear Your lovingkindness in the morning, for in You do I trust; cause me to know the way in which I should walk, for I lift up my soul to You. Deliver me, O LORD, from my enemies; in You I take shelter. Teach me to do Your will, for You are my God; Your Spirit is good. Lead me in the land of uprightness. (Ps. 143:7–10 NKJV)

Tidbits & Morsels: The upside of hitting bottom is you have no place else to go but up.

____

____

____

HOLINESS

You shall be holy to me, for I the LORD am holy and have separated you from the peoples, that you should be mine. (Lev. 20:26 ESV)

For just as you once presented your members as slaves to impurity and to lawlessness leading to more lawlessness, so now present your members as slaves to righteousness leading to sanctification. (Rom. 6:19 ESV)

Think straight. Awaken to the holiness of life. No more playing fast and loose with resurrection facts. Ignorance

> of God is a luxury you can't afford in times like these. Aren't you embarrassed that you've let this kind of thing go on as long as you have? (1 Cor. 15:34 MSG)

> Having such great promises as these, dear friends, let us turn away from everything wrong, whether of body or spirit, and purify ourselves, living in the wholesome fear of God, giving ourselves to him alone. (2 Cor. 7:1 TLB)

> For God has not called us for impurity, but in holiness. Therefore whoever disregards this, disregards not man but God, who gives his Holy Spirit to you. (1 Thess. 4:7–8 ESV)

> Don't lazily slip back into those old grooves of evil, doing just what you feel like doing. You didn't know any better then; you do now. As obedient children, let yourselves be pulled into a way of life shaped by God's life, a life energetic and blazing with holiness. God said, "I am holy; you be holy." (1 Pet. 1:14–16 MSG)

Tidbits & Morsels: Is "holy" a word others would use to describe you? Why or why not?

____

____

____

Holy Spirit

> "As for me, this is my promise to them," says the Lord: "My Holy Spirit shall not leave them, and they shall want the good and hate the wrong—they and their children and their children's children forever." (Isa. 59:21 TLB)

> [Jesus] If you love me, obey my commandments. And I will ask the Father, and he will give you another

> Advocate, who will never leave you. He is the Holy Spirit, who leads into all truth. The world cannot receive him, because it isn't looking for him and doesn't recognize him. But you know him, because he lives with you now and later will be in you. (John 14:15–17 NLT)

> So then, those who are in the flesh cannot please God. But you are not in the flesh but in the Spirit, if indeed the Spirit of God dwells in you. Now if anyone does not have the Spirit of Christ, he is not His. And if Christ is in you, the body is dead because of sin, but the Spirit is life because of righteousness. But if the Spirit of Him who raised Jesus from the dead dwells in you, He who raised Christ from the dead will also give life to your mortal bodies through His Spirit who dwells in you. ... The Spirit Himself bears witness with our spirit that we are children of God, and if children, then heirs—heirs of God and joint heirs with Christ, if indeed we suffer with Him, that we may also be glorified together. (Rom. 8:8–11, 16–17 NKJV)

> And because you are sons, God has sent forth the Spirit of His Son into your hearts, crying out, "Abba, Father!" (Gal. 4:6 NKJV)

Tidbits & Morsels: Do you know the difference between your conscience and the Holy Spirit? Your conscience nags; the Holy Spirit nudges.

____

____

____

Honesty & Truth

> You [the Lord] deserve honesty from the heart; yes, utter sincerity and truthfulness. Oh, give me this wisdom. (Ps. 51:6 TLB)

> Lying lips are an abomination to the LORD, but those who act faithfully are his delight. (Prov. 12:22 ESV)

> Buy the truth and do not sell it—wisdom, instruction and insight as well. (Prov. 23:23 NIV)

> Since God has so generously let us in on what he is doing, we're not about to throw up our hands and walk off the job just because we run into occasional hard times. We refuse to wear masks and play games. We don't maneuver and manipulate behind the scenes. And we don't twist God's Word to suit ourselves. Rather, we keep everything we do and say out in the open, the whole truth on display, so that those who want to can see and judge for themselves in the presence of God. (2 Cor. 4:1–2 MSG)

> Stop lying to each other; tell the truth, for we are parts of each other and when we lie to each other we are hurting ourselves. (Eph. 4:25 TLB)

> Don't lie to each other, for you have stripped off your old sinful nature and all its wicked deeds. Put on your new nature and be renewed as you learn to know your Creator and become like him. (Col. 3:9–10 NLT)

Tidbits & Morsels: Don't rationalize or lie. Even you don't believe some of the whoppers you tell yourself.

____

____

____

Hope

> Though he slay me, yet will I hope in him; I will surely defend my ways to his face. (Job 13:15 NIV)

> Lead me; teach me; for you are the God who gives me salvation. I have no hope except in you. (Ps. 25:5 TLB)

And now, Lord, what do I wait for? My hope is in You. (Ps. 39:7 NKJV)

Hope deferred makes the heart sick, but a desire fulfilled is a tree of life. (Prov. 13:12 ESV)

Surely there is a future, and your hope will not be cut off. (Prov. 23:18 ESV)

But blessed are those who trust in the LORD and have made the LORD their hope and confidence. They are like trees planted along a riverbank, with roots that reach deep into the water. Such trees are not bothered by the heat or worried by long months of drought. Their leaves stay green, and they never stop producing fruit. (Jer. 17:7–8 NLT)

For I know the plans I have for you, declares the LORD, plans for welfare and not for evil, to give you a future and a hope. (Jer. 29:11 ESV)

But me, I'm not giving up. I'm sticking around to see what God will do. I'm waiting for God to make things right. I'm counting on God to listen to me. (Mic. 7:7 MSG)

Then, when that happens, we are able to hold our heads high no matter what happens and know that all is well, for we know how dearly God loves us, and we feel this warm love everywhere within us because God has given us the Holy Spirit to fill our hearts with his love. (Rom. 5:5 TLB)

For in this hope we were saved. Now hope that is seen is not hope. For who hopes for what he sees? But if we hope for what we do not see, we wait for it with patience. (Rom. 8:24–25 ESV)

Tidbits & Morsels: Hope is not a noun or even a feeling; it's an action verb.

Humility

When I consider your heavens, the work of your fingers, the moon and the stars, which you have set in place, what is mankind that you are mindful of them, human beings that you care for them? (Ps. 8:3–4 NIV)

The reward for humility and fear of the Lord is riches and honor and life. (Prov. 22:4 ESV)

Don't work yourself into the spotlight; don't push your way into the place of prominence. It's better to be promoted to a place of honor than face humiliation by being demoted. (Prov. 25:6–7 MSG)

[Jesus] Be especially careful when you are trying to be good so that you don't make a performance out of it. It might be good theater, but the God who made you won't be applauding. When you do something for someone else, don't call attention to yourself. (Matt. 6:1–2 MSG)

[Jesus] At that time the disciples came to Jesus, saying, "Who is the greatest in the kingdom of heaven?" And calling to him a child, he put him in the midst of them and said, "Truly, I say to you, unless you turn and become like children, you will never enter the kingdom of heaven. Whoever humbles himself like this child is the greatest in the kingdom of heaven." (Matt. 18:1–4 ESV)

Humble yourselves, therefore, under God's mighty hand, that he may lift you up in due time. (1 Pet. 5:6 NIV)

Tidbits & Morsels: Pride tries to do it alone. Humility asks for help.

____

____

____

Hunger & Thirst

You gave them bread from heaven for their hunger and brought water for them out of the rock for their thirst, and you told them to go in to possess the land that you had sworn to give them. (Neh. 9:15 ESV)

The Lord lifts the fallen and those bent beneath their loads. The eyes of all mankind look up to you for help; you give them their food as they need it. You constantly satisfy the hunger and thirst of every living thing. (Ps. 145:14–16 TLB)

Is anyone thirsty? Come and drink—even if you have no money! Come, take your choice of wine or milk—it's all free! Why spend your money on food that does not give you strength? Why pay for food that does you no good? Listen to me, and you will eat what is good. You will enjoy the finest food. (Isa. 55:1–2 NLT)

[Jesus] For I was hungry and you gave me something to eat, I was thirsty and you gave me something to drink, I was a stranger and you invited me in. (Matt. 25:35 NIV)

[Jesus] God blesses you who are hungry now, for you will be satisfied. (Luke 6:21 NLT)

[Jesus] I am the bread of life; whoever comes to me shall not hunger, and whoever believes in me shall never thirst. (John 6:35 ESV)

Tidbits & Morsels: If you neglect to feed your soul and spirit daily, you may overfeed your body.

____

____

____

Idolatry

> You shall not make for yourself a carved image, or any likeness of anything that is in heaven above, or that is in the earth beneath, or that is in the water under the earth. You shall not bow down to them or serve them, for I the LORD your God am a jealous God, visiting the iniquity of the fathers on the children to the third and the fourth generation of those who hate me, but showing steadfast love to thousands of those who love me and keep my commandments. (Ex. 20:4–6 ESV)

> Those who run after other gods will suffer more and more. (Ps. 16:4 NIV)

> All those who make no-god idols don't amount to a thing, and what they work so hard at making is nothing. Their little puppet-gods see nothing and know nothing—they're total embarrassments! Who would bother making gods that can't do anything, that can't "god"? Watch all the no-god worshipers hide their faces in shame. Watch the no-god makers slink off humiliated when their idols fail them. Get them out here in the open. Make them face God-reality. (Isa. 44:9–11 MSG)

> [Jesus] No one can serve two masters. Either you will hate the one and love the other, or you will be devoted to the one and despise the other. You cannot serve both God and money. (Luke 16:13 NIV)

Tidbits & Morsels: Jesus paid your debt in full. Why are you worshipping pie?

Joy & Laughter

I'm thanking you, God, from a full heart, I'm writing the book on your wonders. I'm whistling, laughing, and jumping for joy; I'm singing your song, High God. (Ps. 9:1–2 MSG)

I'm happy from the inside out, and from the outside in, I'm firmly formed. You canceled my ticket to hell—that's not my destination! Now you've got my feet on the life path, all radiant from the shining of your face. Ever since you took my hand, I'm on the right way. (Ps. 16:9–11 MSG)

When Jehovah brought back his exiles to Jerusalem, it was like a dream! How we laughed and sang for joy. And the other nations said, "What amazing things the Lord has done for them." Yes, glorious things! What wonder! What joy! May we be refreshed as by streams in the desert. Those who sow tears shall reap joy. Yes, they go out weeping, carrying seed for sowing, and return singing, carrying their sheaves. (Ps. 126:1–6 TLB)

For everything there is a season, a time for every activity under heaven: ... A time to cry and a time to laugh. A time to grieve and a time to dance. (Eccl. 3:1, 4 NLT)

Go, eat your bread with joy, and drink your wine with a merry heart, for God has already approved what you do. (Eccl. 9:7 ESV)

And the ransomed of the Lord shall return and come to Zion with singing; everlasting joy shall be upon their heads; they shall obtain gladness and joy, and sorrow and sighing shall flee away. (Isa. 51:11 ESV)

Tidbits & Morsels: Life is way more fun when you develop a sense of humor; only then can you laugh at yourself and start all over again.

Judge or Pass Judgment

> [Jesus] Judge not, that you be not judged. For with the judgment you pronounce you will be judged, and with the measure you use it will be measured to you. Why do you see the speck that is in your brother's eye, but do not notice the log that is in your own eye? Or how can you say to your brother, "Let me take the speck out of your eye," when there is the log in your own eye? You hypocrite, first take the log out of your own eye, and then you will see clearly to take the speck out of your brother's eye. (Matt. 7:1–5 ESV)

> So when you, a mere human being, pass judgment on them and yet do the same things, do you think you will escape God's judgment? Or do you show contempt for the riches of his kindness, forbearance and patience, not realizing that God's kindness is intended to lead you to repentance? But because of your stubbornness and your unrepentant heart, you are storing up wrath against yourself for the day of God's wrath, when his righteous judgment will be revealed. (Rom. 2:3–5 NIV)

> As for the one who is weak in faith, welcome him, but not to quarrel over opinions. One person believes he may eat anything, while the weak person eats only vegetables. Let not the one who eats despise the one who abstains, and let not the one who abstains pass judgment on the one who eats, for God has welcomed him. Who are you to pass judgment on the servant of another? It is before his own master that he stands or

falls. And he will be upheld, for the Lord is able to make him stand. (Rom. 14:1–4 ESV)

Warn them before God against pious nitpicking, which chips away at the faith. It just wears everyone out. (2 Tim. 2:14 MSG)

Tidbits & Morsels: Exchange those tempting tidbits of gossip for nourishing morsels of grace.

____

____

____

Keep It Simple

Better to have little, with fear for the LORD, than to have great treasure and inner turmoil. (Prov. 15:16 NLT)

He has told you, O man, what is good; and what does the LORD require of you but to do justice, and to love kindness, and to walk humbly with your God? (Mic. 6:8 ESV)

[Jesus] Say just a simple "Yes, I will" or "No, I won't." Your word is enough. To strengthen your promise with a vow shows that something is wrong. (Matt. 5:37 TLB)

[Jesus] Jesus now called the Twelve and gave them authority and power to deal with all the demons and cure diseases. He commissioned them to preach the news of God's kingdom and heal the sick. He said, "Don't load yourselves up with equipment. Keep it simple; you are the equipment. And no luxury inns—get a modest place and be content there until you leave. If you're not welcomed, leave town. Don't make a scene. Shrug your shoulders and move on." (Luke 9:1–5 MSG)

I do want to point out, friends, that time is of the essence. There is no time to waste, so don't complicate

> your lives unnecessarily. Keep it simple—in marriage, grief, joy, whatever. Even in ordinary things—your daily routines of shopping, and so on. Deal as sparingly as possible with the things the world thrusts on you. This world as you see it is fading away. (1 Cor. 7:29–31 MSG)

Tidbits & Morsels: Eat more whole, single ingredient foods. You might discover real flavor under all those condiments, sauces, and toppings.

____

____

____

Laziness

> I went by the field of the lazy man, and by the vineyard of the man devoid of understanding; and there it was, all overgrown with thorns; its surface was covered with nettles; its stone wall was broken down. When I saw it, I considered it well; I looked on it and received instruction: A little sleep, a little slumber, a little folding of the hands to rest; so shall your poverty come like a prowler, and your need like an armed man. (Prov. 24:30–34 NKJV)

> As a door turns on its hinges, so a sluggard turns on his bed. A sluggard buries his hand in the dish; he is too lazy to bring it back to his mouth. (Prov. 26:14–15 NIV)

> The sin of your sister Sodom was this: She lived with her daughters in the lap of luxury—proud, gluttonous, and lazy. They ignored the oppressed and the poor. They put on airs and lived obscene lives. And you know what happened: I did away with them. (Ezek. 16:49–50 MSG)

> We do not want you to become lazy, but to imitate those who through faith and patience inherit what has been promised. (Heb. 6:12 NIV)

Remember, it is sin to know what you ought to do and then not do it. (James 4:17 NLT)

Tidbits & Morsels: Begin this new hunger-satisfied way of eating today. Don't mull over your decision until Monday ... or until the first of the month ... or until after the holidays ... or three months before summer. Get on with it!

LIVE & LET LIVE

He who passes by and meddles in a quarrel not his own is like one who takes a dog by the ears. (Prov. 26:17 NKJV)

For instance, a person who has been around for a while might well be convinced that he can eat anything on the table, while another, with a different background, might assume he should only be a vegetarian and eat accordingly. But since both are guests at Christ's table, wouldn't it be terribly rude if they fell to criticizing what the other ate or didn't eat? God, after all, invited them both to the table. Do you have any business crossing people off the guest list or interfering with God's welcome? If there are corrections to be made or manners to be learned, God can handle that without your help. (Rom. 14:2–4 MSG)

Only let each person lead the life that the Lord has assigned to him, and to which God has called him. (1 Cor. 7:17 ESV)

This should be your ambition: to live a quiet life, minding your own business and doing your own work, just as we told you before. As a result, people who are

> not Christians will trust and respect you, and you will not need to depend on others for enough money to pay your bills. (1 Thess. 4:11–12 TLB)

Tidbits & Morsels: Keep your opinion to yourself ... unless someone asks for it. Even then, you're taking a risk ... unless you tell them exactly what they want to hear.

____

____

____

Loneliness

> And the Lord, He is the One who goes before you. He will be with you, He will not leave you nor forsake you; do not fear nor be dismayed. (Deut. 31:8 NKJV)

> Turn to me and be gracious to me, for I am lonely and afflicted. The troubles of my heart are enlarged; bring me out of my distresses. (Ps. 25:16–17 ESV)

> Father to the fatherless, defender of widows—this is God, whose dwelling is holy. God places the lonely in families; he sets the prisoners free and gives them joy. (Ps. 68:5–6 NLT)

> I am like an owl in the desert, like a little owl in a far-off wilderness. I lie awake, lonely as a solitary bird on the roof. (Ps. 102:6–7 NLT)

> [Jesus] I will not leave you as orphans; I will come to you. (John 14:18 ESV)

> Even before he made the world, God loved us and chose us in Christ to be holy and without fault in his eyes. God decided in advance to adopt us into his own family by bringing us to himself through Jesus Christ. This is

what he wanted to do, and it gave him great pleasure. So we praise God for the glorious grace he has poured out on us who belong to his dear Son. (Eph. 1:4–6 NLT)

Tidbits & Morsels: Wandering around the house restless and alone? Take a long, hot shower—not a bath. Why? You're not apt to eat in the shower, but you might in a tub.

Love

Better a bread crust shared in love than a slab of prime rib served in hate. (Prov. 15:17 MSG)

[Jesus] You shall love the Lord your God with all your heart and with all your soul and with all your mind. This is the great and first commandment. And a second is like it: You shall love your neighbor as yourself. (Matt. 22:37–39 ESV)

[Jesus] For God so loved the world, that he gave his only Son, that whoever believes in him should not perish but have eternal life. For God did not send his Son into the world to condemn the world, but in order that the world might be saved through him. (John 3:16–17 ESV)

If I speak in the tongues of men or of angels, but do not have love, I am only a resounding gong or a clanging cymbal. If I have the gift of prophecy and can fathom all mysteries and all knowledge, and if I have a faith that can move mountains, but do not have love, I am nothing. If I give all I possess to the poor and give over my body to hardship that I may boast, but do not have love, I gain nothing. Love is patient, love is kind. It does not envy, it does not boast, it is not proud. It does not dishonor others, it is not self-seeking, it is

> not easily angered, it keeps no record of wrongs. Love does not delight in evil but rejoices with the truth. It always protects, always trusts, always hopes, always perseveres. Love never fails. (1 Cor. 13:1–8 NIV)

> If you've gotten anything at all out of following Christ, if his love has made any difference in your life, if being in a community of the Spirit means anything to you, if you have a heart, if you care—then do me a favor: Agree with each other, love each other, be deep-spirited friends. Don't push your way to the front; don't sweet-talk your way to the top. Put yourself aside, and help others get ahead. Don't be obsessed with getting your own advantage. Forget yourselves long enough to lend a helping hand. (Phil. 2:1–4 MSG)

> And this is love, that we walk according to his commandments; this is the commandment, just as you have heard from the beginning, so that you should walk in it. (2 John 6 ESV)

Tidbits & Morsels: Be kind to others—and to yourself. No body shaming allowed!

____

____

____

Maintaining Weight Loss

> For the Lord your God is bringing you into a good land of brooks, pools, gushing springs, valleys, and hills; it is a land of wheat and barley, of grapevines, fig trees, pomegranates, olives, and honey; it is a land where food is plentiful, and nothing is lacking; it is a land where iron is as common as stone, and copper is abundant in the hills. When you have eaten your fill, bless the Lord your God for the good land he has given

you. But that is the time to be careful! Beware that in your plenty you don't forget the Lord your God and begin to disobey him. (Deut. 8:7–11 TLB)

I keep my eyes always on the LORD. With him at my right hand, I will not be shaken. (Ps. 16:8 NIV)

[Jesus] When an evil spirit leaves a person, it goes into the desert, seeking rest but finding none. Then it says, "I will return to the person I came from." So it returns and finds its former home empty, swept, and in order. Then the spirit finds seven other spirits more evil than itself, and they all enter the person and live there. And so that person is worse off than before. (Matt. 12:43–45 NLT)

Every athlete exercises self-control in all things. They do it to receive a perishable wreath, but we an imperishable. So I do not run aimlessly; I do not box as one beating the air. But I discipline my body and keep it under control, lest after preaching to others I myself should be disqualified. (1 Cor. 9:25–27 ESV)

But I say, walk by the Spirit, and you will not gratify the desires of the flesh. For the desires of the flesh are against the Spirit, and the desires of the Spirit are against the flesh, for these are opposed to each other, to keep you from doing the things you want to do. (Gal. 5:16–17 ESV)

Therefore, since Christ suffered in his body, arm yourselves also with the same attitude, because whoever suffers in the body is done with sin. As a result, they do not live the rest of their earthly lives for evil human desires, but rather for the will of God. (1 Pet. 4:1–2 NIV)

Tidbits & Morsels: Keep doing what works! Focus on God and his Word, not on your weight or your size.

____

____

____

Making Comparisons

In this way we are like the various parts of a human body. Each part gets its meaning from the body as a whole, not the other way around. The body we're talking about is Christ's body of chosen people. Each of us finds our meaning and function as a part of his body. But as a chopped-off finger or cut-off toe we wouldn't amount to much, would we? So since we find ourselves fashioned into all these excellently formed and marvelously functioning parts in Christ's body, let's just go ahead and be what we were made to be, without enviously or pridefully comparing ourselves with each other, or trying to be something we aren't. (Rom. 12:4–6 MSG)

Not that we dare to classify or compare ourselves with some of those who are commending themselves. But when they measure themselves by one another and compare themselves with one another, they are without understanding. But we will not boast beyond limits but will boast only with regard to the area of influence God assigned to us, to reach even to you. ... "Let the one who boasts, boast in the Lord." For it is not the one who commends himself who is approved, but the one whom the Lord commends. (2 Cor. 10:12–13, 17–18 ESV)

If you think you are too important to help someone, you are only fooling yourself. You are not that important. Pay careful attention to your own work, for then you will get the satisfaction of a job well done, and you won't need to compare yourself to anyone else. For we are each responsible for our own conduct. (Gal. 6:3–5 NLT)

Tidbits & Morsels: Don't compare your progress to that of another. Spiritual progress often comes before physical progress.

____

____

____

Maturity

[Paul] I'm not writing all this as a neighborhood scold to shame you. I'm writing as a father to you, my children. I love you and want you to grow up well, not spoiled. There are a lot of people around who can't wait to tell you what you've done wrong, but there aren't many fathers willing to take the time and effort to help you grow up. It was as Jesus helped me proclaim God's Message to you that I became your father. I'm not, you know, asking you to do anything I'm not already doing myself. (1 Cor. 4:14–16 MSG)

Then we will no longer be infants, tossed back and forth by the waves, and blown here and there by every wind of teaching and by the cunning and craftiness of people in their deceitful scheming. Instead, speaking the truth in love, we will grow to become in every respect the mature body of him who is the head, that is, Christ. (Eph. 4:14–15 NIV)

We teach in a spirit of profound common sense so that we can bring each person to maturity. (Col. 1:28 MSG)

My counsel for you is simple and straightforward: Just go ahead with what you've been given. You received Christ Jesus, the Master; now live him. You're deeply rooted in him. You're well constructed upon him. You know your way around the faith. Now do what you've been taught. School's out; quit studying the subject

> and start living it! And let your living spill over into thanksgiving. (Col. 2:6–7 MSG)

> About this we have much to say, and it is hard to explain, since you have become dull of hearing. For though by this time you ought to be teachers, you need someone to teach you again the basic principles of the oracles of God. You need milk, not solid food, for everyone who lives on milk is unskilled in the word of righteousness, since he is a child. But solid food is for the mature, for those who have their powers of discernment trained by constant practice to distinguish good from evil. (Heb. 5:11–14 ESV)

Tidbits & Morsels: Little babies are cute; big babies are not. Stop being a big baby.

____

____

____

Meditate on the Lord & His Word

> This Book of the Law shall not depart from your mouth, but you shall meditate on it day and night, so that you may be careful to do according to all that is written in it. For then you will make your way prosperous, and then you will have good success. (Josh. 1:8 ESV)

> Oh, the joys of those who do not follow evil men's advice, who do not hang around with sinners, scoffing at the things of God. But they delight in doing everything God wants them to, and day and night are always meditating on his laws and thinking about ways to follow him more closely. (Ps. 1:1–2 TLB)

> Let the words of my mouth and the meditation of my heart be acceptable in your sight, O Lord, my rock and my redeemer. (Ps. 19:14 ESV)

I have thought much about your words and stored them in my heart so that they would hold me back from sin. (Ps. 119:11 TLB)

I remember the days of old; I meditate on all that you have done; I ponder the work of your hands. (Ps. 143:5 ESV)

My son, if you receive my words and treasure up my commandments with you, making your ear attentive to wisdom and inclining your heart to understanding; yes, if you call out for insight and raise your voice for understanding, if you seek it like silver and search for it as for hidden treasures, then you will understand the fear of the LORD and find the knowledge of God. (Prov. 2:1–5 ESV)

Tidbits & Morsels: Start each morning in the Word of God, either reading, hearing, and/or speaking verses aloud. Then quiet yourself and listen for God's voice.

MERCY

O Lord, don't hold back your tender mercies from me! My only hope is in your love and faithfulness. Otherwise I perish, for problems far too big for me to solve are piled higher than my head. Meanwhile my sins, too many to count, have all caught up with me, and I am ashamed to look up. My heart quails within me. Please, Lord, rescue me! Quick! Come and help me! (Ps. 40:11–13 TLB)

Be merciful to me, O God, be merciful to me, for in you my soul takes refuge; in the shadow of your wings I will take refuge, till the storms of destruction pass by. (Ps. 57:1 ESV)

The steadfast love of the LORD never ceases; his mercies never come to an end; they are new every morning; great is your faithfulness. (Lam. 3:22–23 ESV)

Blessed are the merciful, for they will be shown mercy. (Matt. 5:7 NIV)

[Jesus] But love your enemies, and do good, and lend, expecting nothing in return, and your reward will be great, and you will be sons of the Most High for he is kind to the ungrateful and the evil. Be merciful, even as your Father is merciful. (Luke 6:35–36 ESV)

We don't have a priest who is out of touch with our reality. He's been through weakness and testing, experienced it all—all but the sin. So let's walk right up to him and get what he is so ready to give. Take the mercy, accept the help. (Heb. 4:15–16 MSG)

Tidbits & Morsels: Before each meal, pray for others who struggle with overeating or other life-dominating sins.

____

____

____

MIND & THOUGHT LIFE

The mind governed by the flesh is death, but the mind governed by the Spirit is life and peace. (Rom. 8:6 NIV)

And do not be conformed to this world, but be transformed by the renewing of your mind, that you may prove what is that good and acceptable and perfect will of God. (Rom. 12:2 NKJV)

For, "Who can know the Lord's thoughts? Who knows enough to teach him?" But we understand these things, for we have the mind of Christ. (2 Cor. 2:16 NLT)

For though we walk in the flesh, we are not waging war according to the flesh. For the weapons of our warfare are not of the flesh but have divine power to destroy strongholds. We destroy arguments and every lofty opinion raised against the knowledge of God, and take every thought captive to obey Christ, being ready to punish every disobedience, when your obedience is complete. (2 Cor. 10:3–6 ESV)

Finally, brothers, whatever is true, whatever is honorable, whatever is just, whatever is pure, whatever is lovely, whatever is commendable, if there is any excellence, if there is anything worthy of praise, think about these things. What you have learned and received and heard and seen in me—practice these things, and the God of peace will be with you. (Phil. 4:8–9 ESV)

Therefore, holy brothers and sisters, who share in the heavenly calling, fix your thoughts on Jesus, whom we acknowledge as our apostle and high priest. (Heb. 3:1 NIV)

Therefore, with minds that are alert and fully sober, set your hope on the grace to be brought to you when Jesus Christ is revealed at his coming. As obedient children, do not conform to the evil desires you had when you lived in ignorance. But just as he who called you is holy, so be holy in all you do; for it is written: "Be holy, because I am holy." (1 Pet. 1:13–16 NIV)

Tidbits & Morsels: When you talk about food all the time, you think about food all the time. When you think about food all the time ... [Fill in the blank.]

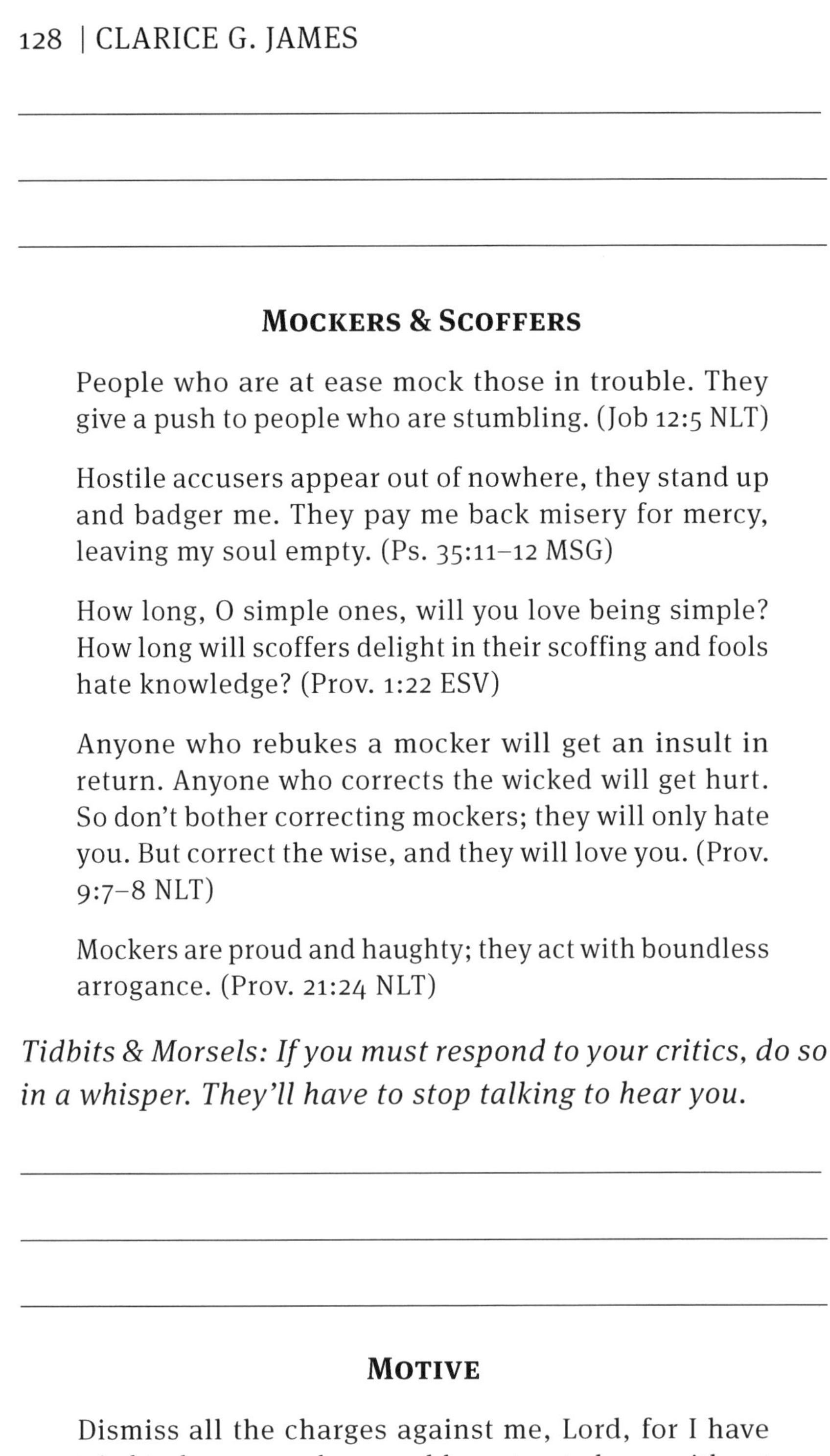

Mockers & Scoffers

People who are at ease mock those in trouble. They give a push to people who are stumbling. (Job 12:5 NLT)

Hostile accusers appear out of nowhere, they stand up and badger me. They pay me back misery for mercy, leaving my soul empty. (Ps. 35:11–12 MSG)

How long, O simple ones, will you love being simple? How long will scoffers delight in their scoffing and fools hate knowledge? (Prov. 1:22 ESV)

Anyone who rebukes a mocker will get an insult in return. Anyone who corrects the wicked will get hurt. So don't bother correcting mockers; they will only hate you. But correct the wise, and they will love you. (Prov. 9:7–8 NLT)

Mockers are proud and haughty; they act with boundless arrogance. (Prov. 21:24 NLT)

Tidbits & Morsels: If you must respond to your critics, do so in a whisper. They'll have to stop talking to hear you.

Motive

Dismiss all the charges against me, Lord, for I have tried to keep your laws and have trusted you without wavering. Cross-examine me, O Lord, and see that this is so; test my motives and affections too. (Ps. 26:1–2 TLB)

All a person's ways seem pure to them, but motives are weighed by the LORD. (Prov. 16:2 NIV)

A bad motive can't achieve a good end; double-talk brings you double trouble. (Prov. 17:20 MSG)

And whatever you do, in word or deed, do everything in the name of the Lord Jesus, giving thanks to God the Father through him. (Col. 3:17 ESV)

For the word of God is living and active, sharper than any two-edged sword, piercing to the division of soul and of spirit, of joints and of marrow, and discerning the thoughts and intentions of the heart. And no creature is hidden from his sight, but all are naked and exposed to the eyes of him to whom we must give account. (Heb. 4:12–13 ESV)

What causes quarrels and what causes fights among you? Is it not this, that your passions are at war within you? You desire and do not have, so you murder. You covet and cannot obtain, so you fight and quarrel. You do not have, because you do not ask. You ask and do not receive, because you ask wrongly, to spend it on your passions. (James 4:1–3 ESV)

Tidbits & Morsels: Ask God to reveal, clarify, and purify your motives; and when he does, please don't try to argue with him.

____

____

____

Obedience

And now, Israel, what does the Lord your God require of you, but to fear the Lord your God, to walk in all his ways, to love him, to serve the Lord your God with all your heart and with all your soul, and to keep the commandments and statutes of the Lord, which I am commanding you today for your good? (Deut. 10:12–13 ESV)

For this commandment that I command you today is not too hard for you, neither is it far off. It is not in heaven, that you should say, "Who will ascend to heaven for us and bring it to us, that we may hear it and do it?" Neither is it beyond the sea, that you should say, "Who will go over the sea for us and bring it to us, that we may hear it and do it?" But the word is very near you. It is in your mouth and in your heart, so that you can do it. (Deut. 30:11–14 ESV)

Does the Lord delight in burnt offerings and sacrifices as much as in obeying the Lord? To obey is better than sacrifice, and to heed is better than the fat of rams. (1 Sam. 15:22 NIV)

The Lord is good and glad to teach the proper path to all who go astray; he will teach the ways that are right and best to those who humbly turn to him. And when we obey him, every path he guides us on is fragrant with his loving-kindness and his truth. (Ps. 25:8–10 TLB)

Here is my final conclusion: fear God and obey his commandments, for this is the entire duty of man. For God will judge us for everything we do, including every hidden thing, good or bad. (Eccl. 12:13–14 TLB)

[Jesus]: If you keep my commandments, you will abide in my love, just as I have kept my Father's commandments and abide in his love. (John 15:10 ESV)

For this is the love of God, that we keep his commandments. And his commandments are not burdensome. For everyone who has been born of God overcomes the world. And this is the victory that has overcome the world—our faith. Who is it that overcomes the world except the one who believes that Jesus is the Son of God? (1 John 5:3–5 ESV)

Tidbits & Morsels: Give your tongue a daily workout. Practice saying, "No, thank you," "Not right now," or "Maybe later."

____

____

____

One Day at a Time

Teach us to number our days and recognize how few they are; help us to spend them as we should. (Ps. 90:12 TLB)

This is the day that the Lord has made; let us rejoice and be glad in it. (Ps. 118:24 ESV)

Don't brashly announce what you're going to do tomorrow; you don't know the first thing about tomorrow. (Prov. 27:1 MSG)

[Jesus] So don't be anxious about tomorrow. God will take care of your tomorrow too. Live one day at a time. (Matt. 6:34 TLB)

[Jesus] Give us each day our daily bread. (Luke 11:3 ESV)

But, beloved, do not forget this one thing, that with the Lord one day is as a thousand years, and a thousand years as one day. (2 Pet. 3:8 NKJV)

Tidbits & Morsels: Just for today, breathe in and breathe out and appreciate the many blessings you have from God.

____

____

____

Pain & Suffering

At least I can take comfort in this: Despite the pain, I have not denied the words of the Holy One. (Job 6:10 NLT)

For I [Paul] consider that the sufferings of this present time are not worthy to be compared with the glory which shall be revealed in us. (Rom. 8:18 NKJV)

For this light momentary affliction is preparing for us an eternal weight of glory beyond all comparison, as we look not to the things that are seen but to the things that are unseen. For the things that are seen are transient, but the things that are unseen are eternal. (2 Cor. 4:17–18 ESV)

For it is better to suffer for doing good, if that should be God's will, than for doing evil. (1 Pet. 3:17 ESV)

So then, since Christ suffered physical pain, you must arm yourselves with the same attitude he had, and be ready to suffer, too. For if you have suffered physically for Christ, you have finished with sin. You won't spend the rest of your lives chasing your own desires, but you will be anxious to do the will of God. You have had enough in the past of the evil things that godless people enjoy—their immorality and lust, their feasting and drunkenness and wild parties, and their terrible worship of idols. Of course, your former friends are surprised when you no longer plunge into the flood of wild and destructive things they do. So they slander you. (1 Pet. 4:1–4 NLT)

Tidbits & Morsels: Ask God to ship your baggage—same day delivery and free—as far as the east is from the west.

____

____

____

Patience

Wait for the Lord; be strong and let your heart take courage; wait for the Lord! (Ps. 27:14 ESV)

Be still in the presence of the Lord, and wait patiently for him to act. Don't worry about evil people who prosper or fret about their wicked schemes. (Ps. 37:7 NLT)

I waited patiently for the Lord; he inclined to me and heard my cry. He drew me up from the pit of destruction, out of the miry bog, and set my feet upon a rock, making my steps secure. (Ps. 40:1–2 ESV)

A person's wisdom yields patience; it is to one's glory to overlook an offense. (Prov. 19:11 NIV)

Finishing is better than starting. Patience is better than pride. (Eccl. 7:8 NLT)

Yet the Lord still waits for you to come to him so he can show you his love; he will conquer you to bless you, just as he said. For the Lord is faithful to his promises. Blessed are all those who wait for him to help them. (Isa. 30:18 TLB)

Bear in mind that our Lord's patience means salvation, just as our dear brother Paul also wrote you with the wisdom that God gave him. (2 Pet. 3:15 NIV)

Tidbits & Morsels: Is it reasonable to expect to lose weight faster than you put it on? If you lose gradually (about 1 to 2 pounds per week), you're more likely to keep it off.

____

____

____

Peace

> Those who love your laws have great peace of heart and mind and do not stumble. (Ps. 119:165 TLB)
>
> You keep him in perfect peace whose mind is stayed on you, because he trusts in you. (Isa. 26:3 ESV)
>
> The fruit of that righteousness will be peace; its effect will be quietness and confidence forever. (Isa. 32:17 NIV)
>
> [Jesus] Peace I leave with you; my peace I give to you. Not as the world gives do I give to you. Let not your hearts be troubled, neither let them be afraid. (John 14:27 ESV)
>
> Repay no one evil for evil but give thought to do what is honorable in the sight of all. If possible, so far as it depends on you, live peaceably with all. (Rom. 12:17–18 ESV)
>
> And let the peace of Christ rule in your hearts, to which indeed you were called in one body. And be thankful. (Col. 3:15 ESV)
>
> Pursue peace with all people, and holiness, without which no one will see the Lord. (Heb. 12:14 NKJV)

Tidbits & Morsels: Relax. Enjoy a cup of tea, a cozy chair, and a Good Book.

___

___

___

Peer Pressure

You must not follow the crowd in doing wrong. When you are called to testify in a dispute, do not be swayed by the crowd to twist justice. (Ex. 23:2 NLT)

The godly give good advice to their friends; the wicked lead them astray. (Prov. 12:26 NLT)

Whoever misleads the upright into an evil way will fall into his own pit, but the blameless will have a goodly inheritance. (Prov. 28:10 ESV)

[Jesus] "There will always be temptations to sin," Jesus said one day to his disciples, "but woe to the man who does the tempting." (Luke 17:1 TLB)

Do not be deceived: "Bad company ruins good morals." (1 Cor. 15:33 ESV)

Dear friend, don't let this bad example influence you. Follow only what is good. Remember that those who do what is right prove that they are God's children; and those who continue in evil prove that they are far from God. (3 John 11 TLB)

Tidbits & Morsels: Don't let others sway you. Take charge of the company you keep and the foods you eat.

___

___

___

People-pleasing

Why haven't you obeyed the Lord? Why did you rush for the plunder and do what was evil in the Lord's sight?" "But I did obey the Lord," Saul insisted. "I carried out the mission he gave me. I brought back King Agag, but I destroyed everyone else. Then my troops brought in the best of the sheep, goats, cattle, and plunder to sacrifice to the Lord your God in Gilgal." But Samuel replied, "What is more pleasing to the Lord: your burnt offerings and sacrifices or your obedience to his voice? Listen! Obedience is better than sacrifice, and submission is better than offering the fat of rams. Rebellion is as sinful as witchcraft, and stubbornness as bad as worshiping idols. So because you have rejected the command of the Lord, he has rejected you as king." Then Saul admitted to Samuel, "Yes, I have sinned. I have disobeyed your instructions and the Lord's command, for I was afraid of the people and did what they demanded. (1 Sam. 15:19–24 NLT)

The Lord is with me; I will not be afraid. What can mere mortals do to me? The Lord is with me; he is my helper. I look in triumph on my enemies. It is better to take refuge in the Lord than to trust in humans. (Ps. 118:6–8 NIV)

Quit scraping and fawning over mere humans, so full of themselves, so full of hot air! Can't you see there's nothing to them? (Isa. 2:22 MSG)

Nevertheless, many even of the authorities believed in him [Jesus], but for fear of the Pharisees they did not confess it, so that they would not be put out of the synagogue; for they loved the glory that comes from man more than the glory that comes from God. (John 12:42–43 ESV)

For am I now seeking the approval of man, or of God? Or am I trying to please man? If I were still trying to please man, I would not be a servant of Christ. (Gal. 1:10 ESV)

For our appeal does not spring from error or impurity or any attempt to deceive, but just as we have been approved by God to be entrusted with the gospel, so we speak, not to please man, but to please God who tests our hearts. (1 Thess. 2:3–4 ESV)

Tidbits & Morsels: Just because everybody's doing it doesn't mean you have to. What? Your mother never told you that?

Persecution

Job answered: "How long are you going to keep battering away at me, pounding me with these harangues? Time after time after time you jump all over me. Do you have no conscience, abusing me like this? Even if I have, somehow or other, gotten off the track, what business is that of yours? Why do you insist on putting me down, using my troubles as a stick to beat me? Tell it to God—he's the one behind all this, he's the one who dragged me into this mess." (Job 19:1–6 MSG)

Hostile accusers appear out of nowhere, they stand up and badger me. They pay me back misery for mercy, leaving my soul empty. (Ps. 35:11–12 MSG)

My tears have been my food day and night, while people say to me all day long, "Where is your God?" (Ps. 42:3 ESV)

> [Jesus] And these are the ones sown on rocky ground: the ones who, when they hear the word, immediately receive it with joy. And they have no root in themselves, but endure for a while; then, when tribulation or persecution arises on account of the word, immediately they fall away. (Mark 4:16–17 ESV)

> We are hard pressed on every side, but not crushed; perplexed, but not in despair; persecuted, but not abandoned; struck down, but not destroyed. (2 Cor. 4:8–9 NIV)

> But it is no shame to suffer for being a Christian. Praise God for the privilege of being called by his name! (1 Pet. 4:16 NLT)

Tidbits & Morsels: Family may badger you about your new hunger-satisfied way of eating. But remember, no matter what Granny says, holiday [food] traditions are not holy [food] commandments.

____

____

____

PERSEVERANCE

> March on with courage, my soul! (Judg. 5:21 NLT)

> Don't be impatient for the Lord to act! Keep traveling steadily along his pathway and in due season he will honor you with every blessing, and you will see the wicked destroyed. (Ps. 37:34 TLB)

> People with their minds set on you [God], you keep completely whole, steady on their feet, because they keep at it and don't quit. Depend on GOD and keep at it because in the LORD GOD you have a sure thing. (Isa.

26:3–4 MSG)

Not that I [Paul] have already obtained this or am already perfect, but I press on to make it my own, because Christ Jesus has made me his own. Brothers, I do not consider that I have made it my own. But one thing I do: forgetting what lies behind and straining forward to what lies ahead, I press on toward the goal for the prize of the upward call of God in Christ Jesus. Let those of us who are mature think this way, and if in anything you think otherwise, God will reveal that also to you. (Phil. 3:12–15 ESV)

Therefore, since we are surrounded by such a great cloud of witnesses, let us throw off everything that hinders and the sin that so easily entangles. And let us run with perseverance the race marked out for us, fixing our eyes on Jesus, the pioneer and perfecter of faith. For the joy set before him he endured the cross, scorning its shame, and sat down at the right hand of the throne of God. Consider him who endured such opposition from sinners, so that you will not grow weary and lose heart. (Heb. 12:1–3 NIV)

Tidbits & Morsels: To limit impulse buying, keep your eyes front and center in checkout lanes. Even hardware store snacks can trip you up!

____

____

____

Physical Body

For you created my inmost being; you knit me together in my mother's womb. I praise you because I am fearfully and wonderfully made; your works are wonderful, I know that full well. (Ps. 139:13–14 NIV)

I appeal to you therefore, brothers, by the mercies of God, to present your bodies as a living sacrifice, holy and acceptable to God, which is your spiritual worship. (Rom. 12:1 ESV)

For instance, take the matter of eating. God has given us an appetite for food and stomachs to digest it. But that doesn't mean we should eat more than we need. Don't think of eating as important because someday God will do away with both stomachs and food. ... Haven't you yet learned that your body is the home of the Holy Spirit God gave you, and that he lives within you? Your own body does not belong to you. For God has bought you with a great price. So use every part of your body to give glory back to God because he owns it. (1 Cor. 6:13, 19–20 TLB)

The bodies we have now embarrass us, for they become sick and die; but they will be full of glory when we come back to life again. Yes, they are weak, dying bodies now, but when we live again they will be full of strength. (1 Cor. 15:43 TLB)

For we know that if the tent that is our earthly home is destroyed, we have a building from God, a house not made with hands, eternal in the heavens. For in this tent we groan, longing to put on our heavenly dwelling, if indeed by putting it on we may not be found naked. For while we are still in this tent, we groan, being burdened—not that we would be unclothed, but that we would be further clothed, so that what is mortal may be swallowed up by life. He who has prepared us for this very thing is God, who has given us the Spirit as a guarantee. (2 Cor. 5:1–5 ESV)

But there's far more to life for us. We're citizens of high heaven! We're waiting the arrival of the Savior, the Master, Jesus Christ, who will transform our earthy bodies into glorious bodies like his own. He'll make us

> beautiful and whole with the same powerful skill by which he is putting everything as it should be, under and around him. (Phil. 3:20–21 MSG)

Tidbits & Morsels: Your brain sends signals when your body is cold, hot, hungry, thirsty, sick, tired, stuffed, sore, and satisfied. If you pay close attention, your brain will tell you the specific type of nourishment your body needs.

____

____

____

Physical Exercise

> No king succeeds with a big army alone, no warrior wins by brute strength. Horsepower is not the answer; no one gets by on muscle alone. (Ps. 33:16–17 MSG)

> She dresses herself with strength and makes her arms strong. (Prov. 31:17 ESV)

> [Jesus] Jesus then left that part of the country [Jerusalem] and walked the *fifty miles* [Italics mine] to Tyre and Sidon. (Matt. 15:21 TLB)

> In a race everyone runs, but only one person gets first prize. So run your race to win. To win the contest you must deny yourselves many things that would keep you from doing your best. An athlete goes to all this trouble just to win a blue ribbon or a silver cup, but we do it for a heavenly reward that never disappears. So I run straight to the goal with purpose in every step. I fight to win. I'm not just shadow-boxing or playing around. Like an athlete I punish my body, treating it roughly, training it to do what it should, not what it wants to. Otherwise I fear that after enlisting others for the race, I myself might be declared unfit and ordered to stand aside. (1 Cor. 9:24–27 TLB)

> Physical training is good, but training for godliness is much better, promising benefits in this life and in the life to come. (1 Tim. 4:8 NLT)

> An athlete is not crowned unless he competes according to the rules. (2 Tim. 2:5 ESV)

Tidbits & Morsels: Exercise any part of your body that moves. Stand instead of sitting. Walk instead of standing. Run instead of walking. Flap your arms while running. (Just a suggestion.)

____

____

____

Plan & Prepare

> So the men arose and went, and Joshua charged those who went to write the description of the land, saying, "Go up and down in the land and write a description and return to me." (Josh. 18:8 ESV)

> Go to the ant, you sluggard! Consider her ways and be wise, which, having no captain, overseer, or ruler, provides her supplies in the summer, and gathers her food in the harvest. How long will you slumber, O sluggard? When will you rise from your sleep? A little sleep, a little slumber, a little folding of the hands to sleep—so shall your poverty come on you like a prowler, and your need like an armed man. (Prov. 6:6–11 NKJV)

> A wise man thinks ahead; a fool doesn't and even brags about it! (Prov. 13:16 TLB)

> A sensible man watches for problems ahead and prepares to meet them. The simpleton never looks and suffers the consequences. (Prov. 27:12 TLB)

> Then the word of the LORD came by the hand of Haggai the prophet, "Is it a time for you yourselves to dwell in your paneled houses, while this house lies in ruins? Now, therefore, thus says the LORD of hosts: Consider your ways. You have sown much, and harvested little. You eat, but you never have enough; you drink, but you never have your fill. You clothe yourselves, but no one is warm. And he who earns wages does so to put them into a bag with holes." (Hag. 1:3–6 ESV)

Tidbits & Morsels: Be proactive when dining out. Ask for a carry-out container when you place your order.

____

____

____

PRAISE & WORSHIP

> O God, You are my God; early will I seek You; my soul thirsts for You; my flesh longs for You in a dry and thirsty land where there is no water. So I have looked for You in the sanctuary, to see Your power and Your glory. Because Your lovingkindness is better than life, my lips shall praise You. Thus I will bless You while I live; I will lift up my hands in Your name. (Ps. 63:1–4 NKJV)

> Make a joyful noise to the LORD, all the earth! Serve the LORD with gladness! Come into his presence with singing! (Ps. 100:1–2 ESV)

> Praise the LORD! Praise God in his sanctuary; praise him in his mighty heaven! Praise him for his mighty works; praise his unequaled greatness! Praise him with a blast of the ram's horn; praise him with the lyre and harp! Praise him with the tambourine and dancing; praise him with strings and flutes! Praise him with a clash of cymbals; praise him with loud clanging cymbals.

> Let everything that breathes sing praises to the LORD! Praise the LORD! (Ps. 150:1–6 NLT)

> LORD, you are my God; I will exalt you and praise your name, for in perfect faithfulness you have done wonderful things, things planned long ago. (Isa. 25:1 NIV)

> Talk with each other much about the Lord, quoting psalms and hymns and singing sacred songs, making music in your hearts to the Lord. (Eph. 5:19 TLB)

> Since we are receiving a Kingdom that is unshakable, let us be thankful and please God by worshiping him with holy fear and awe. (Heb. 12:28 NLT)

Tidbits & Morsels: You'll lighten your load when you sing praises to God. If you can't sing—hum! If you can't hum, play music and get those endorphins dancing!

____

____

____

PRAYER

> Yet, LORD my God, give attention to your servant's prayer and his plea for mercy. Hear the cry and the prayer that your servant is praying in your presence. (2 Chron. 6:19 NIV)

> In the morning, O LORD, you hear my voice; in the morning I lay my requests before you and wait expectantly. (Ps. 5:3 NIV)

> [Jesus] For where two or three are gathered in my name, there am I among them. (Matt. 18:19–20 ESV)

[Jesus] And rising very early in the morning, while it was still dark, he departed and went out to a desolate place and there he prayed. (Mark 1:35 ESV)

And in the same way—by our faith—the Holy Spirit helps us with our daily problems and in our praying. For we don't even know what we should pray for nor how to pray as we should, but the Holy Spirit prays for us with such feeling that it cannot be expressed in words. (Rom. 8:26 TLB)

Is anyone among you suffering? Let him pray. Is anyone cheerful? Let him sing praise. Is anyone among you sick? Let him call for the elders of the church, and let them pray over him, anointing him with oil in the name of the Lord. And the prayer of faith will save the one who is sick, and the Lord will raise him up. (James 5:13–15 ESV)

And this is the confidence that we have toward him, that if we ask anything according to his will he hears us. And if we know that he hears us in whatever we ask, we know that we have the requests that we have asked of him. (1 John 5:14–15 ESV)

Tidbits & Morsels: Get on your knees—you know, those two bumps between your calves and thighs? Now pray!

____

____

____

Pride

Do not become proud at that time and forget the Lord your God, who rescued you from slavery in the land of Egypt. (Deut. 8:14 NLT)

For you will not delight in sacrifice, or I would give it; you will not be pleased with a burnt offering. The

> sacrifices of God are a broken spirit; a broken and contrite heart, O God, you will not despise. (Ps. 51:16–17 ESV)

> I have been the LORD your God ever since I brought you out of Egypt. You must acknowledge no God but me, for there is no other savior. I took care of you in the wilderness, in that dry and thirsty land. But when you had eaten and were satisfied, you became proud and forgot me. (Hos. 13:4–6 NLT)

> Look at the proud! They trust in themselves, and their lives are crooked. But the righteous will live by their faithfulness to God. (Hab. 2:4 NLT)

> We sometimes tend to think we know all we need to know to answer these kinds of questions—but sometimes our humble hearts can help us more than our proud minds. We never really know enough until we recognize that God alone knows it all. (1 Cor. 8:2–3 MSG)

> So to keep me from becoming conceited because of the surpassing greatness of the revelations, a thorn was given me in the flesh, a messenger of Satan to harass me, to keep me from becoming conceited. Three times I pleaded with the Lord about this, that it should leave me. But he said to me, "My grace is sufficient for you, for my power is made perfect in weakness." Therefore I will boast all the more gladly of my weaknesses, so that the power of Christ may rest upon me. (2 Cor. 12:7–9 ESV)

Tidbits & Morsels: Your pride boasts, "If I had her money, I could lose weight too." Know any wealthy and (still) overweight celebrities? Of course you do. Money is not the answer is it?

____

____

____

PRIORITIES (FIRST THINGS FIRST)

Do your planning and prepare your fields before building your house. (Prov. 24:27 NLT)

[Jesus] But seek first the kingdom of God and his righteousness, and all these things will be added to you. (Matt. 6:33 ESV)

[Jesus] And don't worry about food—what to eat and drink; don't worry at all that God will provide it for you. All mankind scratches for its daily bread, but your heavenly Father knows your needs. He will always give you all you need from day to day if you will make the Kingdom of God your primary concern. (Luke 12:29–31 TLB)

For, after all, the important thing for us as Christians is not what we eat or drink but stirring up goodness and peace and joy from the Holy Spirit. (Rom. 14:17 TLB)

Indeed, I count everything as loss because of the surpassing worth of knowing Christ Jesus my Lord. For his sake I have suffered the loss of all things and count them as rubbish, in order that I may gain Christ and be found in him, not having a righteousness of my own that comes from the law, but that which comes through faith in Christ, the righteousness from God that depends on faith—that I may know him and the power of his resurrection, and may share his sufferings, becoming like him in his death, that by any means possible I may attain the resurrection from the dead. (Phil. 3:8–11 ESV)

Tidbits & Morsels: To avoid grabbing more than you need when hunger strikes, make it a priority to keep a variety of choice foods on hand.

____

____

____

Procrastination

> Then the Lord said to me, "You have been traveling around this mountain country long enough." (Deut. 2:2–3 ESV)
>
> So Joshua said to the people of Israel, "How long will you put off going in to take possession of the land, which the Lord, the God of your fathers, has given you?" (Josh. 18:3 ESV)
>
> When you tell God you'll do something, do it—now. God takes no pleasure in foolish drivel. Vow it, then do it. Far better not to vow in the first place than to vow and not pay up. (Eccl. 5:4–5 MSG)
>
> If you wait for perfect conditions, you will never get anything done. (Eccl. 11:4 TLB)
>
> In light of all this, here's what I [Paul] want you to do. While I'm locked up here, a prisoner for the Master, I want you to get out there and walk—better yet, run!—on the road God called you to travel. I don't want any of you sitting around on your hands. I don't want anyone strolling off, down some path that goes nowhere. And mark that you do this with humility and discipline—not in fits and starts, but steadily, pouring yourselves out for each other in acts of love, alert at noticing differences and quick at mending fences. (Eph. 4:1–3 MSG)

Tidbits & Morsels: Complete a task you've been putting off. The sense of accomplishment will boost your morale.

____

____

____

Progress Not Perfection

> The righteous keep moving forward, and those with clean hands become stronger and stronger. (Job 17:9 NLT)

> Surely there is not a righteous man on earth who does good and never sins. (Eccl. 7:20 ESV)

> I'm not saying that I [Paul] have this all together, that I have it made. But I am well on my way, reaching out for Christ, who has so wondrously reached out for me. Friends, don't get me wrong: By no means do I count myself an expert in all of this, but I've got my eye on the goal, where God is beckoning us onward—to Jesus. I'm off and running, and I'm not turning back. So let's keep focused on that goal, those of us who want everything God has for us. If any of you have something else in mind, something less than total commitment, God will clear your blurred vision—you'll see it yet! Now that we're on the right track, let's stay on it. (Phil. 3:12–16 MSG)

> Let no one despise you for your youth, but set the believers an example in speech, in conduct, in love, in faith, in purity. Until I come, devote yourself to the public reading of Scripture, to exhortation, to teaching. Do not neglect the gift you have, which was given you by prophecy when the council of elders laid their hands on you. Practice these things, immerse yourself in them, so that all may see your progress. (1 Tim. 4:12–15 ESV)

> For we all stumble in many things. If anyone does not stumble in word, he is a perfect man, able also to bridle the whole body. (James 3:2 NKJV)

Tidbits & Morsels: Repeat after me: I am a new creation in Christ ... but God isn't finished with me yet.

Rebellion & Stubbornness

> For rebellion is as bad as the sin of witchcraft, and stubbornness is as bad as worshiping idols. (1 Sam. 15:23 TLB)

> Be not like a horse or a mule, without understanding, which must be curbed with bit and bridle, or it will not stay near you. (Ps. 32:9 ESV)

> Whoever stubbornly refuses to accept criticism will suddenly be destroyed beyond recovery. (Prov. 29:1 NLT)

> "What sorrow awaits my rebellious children," says the Lord. "You make plans that are contrary to mine. You make alliances not directed by my Spirit, thus piling up your sins. For without consulting me, you have gone down to Egypt for help. You have put your trust in Pharaoh's protection. You have tried to hide in his shade. But by trusting Pharaoh, you will be humiliated, and by depending on him, you will be disgraced." (Isa. 30:1–3 NLT)

> [Jesus] Why do you call me, "Lord, Lord," and do not do what I say? ... But the one who hears my words and does not put them into practice is like a man who

built a house on the ground without a foundation. The moment the torrent struck that house, it collapsed and its destruction was complete. (Luke 6:46, 49 NIV)

But no, you won't listen; and so you are saving up terrible punishment for yourselves because of your stubbornness in refusing to turn from your sin; for there is going to come a day of wrath when God will be the just Judge of all the world. (Rom. 2:5 TLB)

Today when you hear his voice, don't harden your hearts as Israel did when they rebelled, when they tested me in the wilderness. (Heb. 3:7–8 NLT)

Tidbits & Morsels: Apologize to someone you have hurt. Now! And mean it.

____

____

____

Recovery & Restoration

And the Lord restored the fortunes of Job, when he had prayed for his friends. And the Lord gave Job twice as much as he had before. ... And the Lord blessed the latter days of Job more than his beginning. (Job 42:10, 12 ESV)

When the Lord restored the fortunes of Zion, we were like those who dream. Then our mouth was filled with laughter, and our tongue with shouts of joy; then they said among the nations, "The Lord has done great things for them." The Lord has done great things for us; we are glad. (Ps. 126:1–3 ESV)

> "But I will restore you to health and heal your wounds," declares the LORD, "because you are called an outcast, Zion for whom no one cares." (Jer. 30:17 NIV)

> Restore us, O LORD, and bring us back to you again! Give us back the joys we once had! (Lam. 5:21 NLT)

> I will restore to you the years that the swarming locust has eaten, the hopper, the destroyer, and the cutter, my great army, which I sent among you. You shall eat in plenty and be satisfied, and praise the name of the LORD your God, who has dealt wondrously with you. And my people shall never again be put to shame. (Joel 2:25–26 ESV)

> And the God of all grace, who called you to his eternal glory in Christ, after you have suffered a little while, will himself restore you and make you strong, firm and steadfast. (1 Pet. 5:10 NIV)

Tidbits & Morsels: Drink water to beat headaches, stave off health threats, and improve your digestive system. PS: The rumor that sipping water between bites will kill you is all wet.

____

____

____

REGRETS & REMORSE

> Oh, that my steps might be steady, keeping to the course you set; then I'd never have any regrets in comparing my life with your counsel. (Ps. 119:5–6 MSG)

> You don't want to end your life full of regrets, nothing but sin and bones, saying, "Oh, why didn't I do what they told me? Why did I reject a disciplined life? Why didn't I listen to my mentors, or take my teachers

seriously? My life is ruined! I haven't one blessed thing to show for my life!" (Prov. 5:11–14 MSG)

Tell them this, GOD's Message: "Do people fall down and not get up? Or take the wrong road and then just keep going? So why does this people go backward, and just keep on going—*backward*! They stubbornly hold on to their illusions, refuse to change direction. I listened carefully but heard not so much as a whisper. No one expressed one word of regret. Not a single 'I'm sorry' did I hear. They just kept at it, blindly and stupidly banging their heads against a brick wall." (Jer. 8:4–6 MSG)

For the kind of sorrow God wants us to experience leads us away from sin and results in salvation. There's no regret for that kind of sorrow. But worldly sorrow, which lacks repentance, results in spiritual death. (2 Cor. 7:10 NLT)

Tidbits & Morsels: Make a list of all the gummy-bear weight-loss supplements you've tried. How'd those yummy gummies work out for you?

___

___

___

REPENTANCE

When I shut up heaven and there is no rain, or command the locusts to devour the land, or send pestilence among My people, if My people who are called by My name will humble themselves, and pray and seek My face, and turn from their wicked ways, then I will hear from heaven, and will forgive their sin and heal their land. (2 Chron. 7:13–14 NKJV)

> This is what the Sovereign LORD, the Holy One of Israel, says: "In repentance and rest is your salvation, in quietness and trust is your strength, but you would have none of it." (Isa. 30:15 NIV)

> "Now, therefore," says the LORD, "Turn to Me with all your heart, with fasting, with weeping, and with mourning." So rend your heart, and not your garments; return to the LORD your God, for He is gracious and merciful, slow to anger, and of great kindness; and He relents from doing harm. (Joel 2:12–13 NKJV)

> Repent, then, and turn to God, so that your sins may be wiped out, that times of refreshing may come from the Lord, and that he may send the Messiah, who has been appointed for you—even Jesus. (Acts 3:19–20 NIV)

> God overlooks it as long as you don't know any better—but that time is past. The unknown is now known, and he's calling for a radical life-change. (Acts 17:30 MSG)

> Do you suppose, O man—you who judge those who practice such things and yet do them yourself—that you will escape the judgment of God? Or do you presume on the riches of his kindness and forbearance and patience, not knowing that God's kindness is meant to lead you to repentance? But because of your hard and impenitent heart you are storing up wrath for yourself on the day of wrath when God's righteous judgment will be revealed. (Rom. 2:3–5 ESV)

Tidbits & Morsels: "I can quit overeating any time," you say. Then why don't you? By the grace of God, turn from your old way of eating and turn to a new way of living.

____

____

____

Rest vs. Restlessness

So the creation of the heavens and the earth and everything in them was completed. On the seventh day God had finished his work of creation, so he rested from all his work. And God blessed the seventh day and declared it holy, because it was the day when he rested from all his work of creation. (Gen. 2:1–3 NLT)

Six days you shall work, but on the seventh day you shall rest. In plowing time and in harvest you shall rest. (Ex. 34:21 ESV)

God's a safe-house for the battered, a sanctuary during bad times. The moment you arrive, you relax; you're never sorry you knocked. (Ps. 9:9–10 MSG)

Better a handful with quietness than both hands full, together with toil and grasping for the wind. (Eccl. 4:6 NKJV)

[Jesus] Come to me and I will give you rest—all of you who work so hard beneath a heavy yoke. Wear my yoke—for it fits perfectly—and let me teach you; for I am gentle and humble, and you shall find rest for your souls; for I give you only light burdens. (Matt. 11:28–30 TLB)

[Jesus] Then Jesus suggested, "Let's get away from the crowds for a while and rest." (Mark 6:31 TLB)

Tidbits & Morsels: Without sufficient rest, your resolve may dissolve.

____

____

____

Results & Rewards

But you—you serve your God and he'll bless your food and your water. (Ex. 23:25 MSG)

The Lord will make you the head, not the tail. If you pay attention to the commands of the Lord your God that I give you this day and carefully follow them, you will always be at the top, never at the bottom. (Deut. 28:13 NIV)

You're blessed when you stay on course, walking steadily on the road revealed by God. You're blessed when you follow his directions, doing your best to find him. That's right—you don't go off on your own; you walk straight along the road he set. You, God, prescribed the right way to live; now you expect us to live it. (Ps. 119:1–4 MSG)

The world of the generous gets larger and larger; the world of the stingy gets smaller and smaller. The one who blesses others is abundantly blessed; those who help others are helped. (Prov. 11:24–25 MSG)

The Spirit of the Sovereign Lord is on me, because the Lord has anointed me to proclaim good news to the poor. ... Instead of your shame you will receive a double portion, and instead of disgrace you will rejoice in your inheritance. And so you will inherit a double portion in your land, and everlasting joy will be yours. (Isa. 61:1, 7 NIV)

[Jesus] And the seeds that fell on the good soil represent honest, good-hearted people who hear God's word, cling to it, and patiently produce a huge harvest. (Luke 8:15 NLT)

And we know that for those who love God all things work together for good, for those who are called according to his purpose. (Rom. 8:28 ESV)

Whatever you do, work heartily, as for the Lord and not for men, knowing that from the Lord you will receive the inheritance as your reward. You are serving the Lord Christ. (Col. 3:23–24 ESV)

And it is impossible to please God without faith. Anyone who wants to come to him must believe that God exists and that he rewards those who sincerely seek him. (Heb. 11:6 NLT)

Tidbits & Morsels: Go on, give that skinny girl a compliment! One day she could be you.

____

____

____

Righteousness

The righteousness of the blameless keeps his way straight, but the wicked falls by his own wickedness. The righteousness of the upright delivers them, but the treacherous are taken captive by their lust. (Prov. 11:5–6 ESV)

The man who tries to be good, loving, and kind finds life, righteousness, and honor. (Prov. 21:21 TLB)

I [the Lord] said, "Plant the good seeds of righteousness, and you will harvest a crop of love. Plow up the hard ground of your hearts, for now is the time to seek the Lord, that he may come and shower righteousness upon you." (Hos. 10:12 NLT)

[Jesus] Blessed are those who hunger and thirst for righteousness, for they shall be filled. (Matt. 5:6 NKJV)

> For Christ has already accomplished the purpose for which the law was given. As a result, all who believe in him are made right with God. (Rom. 10:4 NLT)

> Dear children, don't let anyone deceive you about this: When people do what is right, it shows that they are righteous, even as Christ is righteous. (1 John 3:7 NLT)

Tidbits & Morsels: If you eat while standing, what you eat still stands. Count every lick, pick, taste, bite, and sip while you're cooking.

____

____

____

Sacrifice

> Do you think all God wants are sacrifices—empty rituals just for show? He wants you to listen to him! Plain listening is the thing, not staging a lavish religious production. (1 Sam. 15:22 MSG)

> The one who offers thanksgiving as his sacrifice glorifies me; to one who orders his way rightly I will show the salvation of God! (Ps. 50:23 ESV)

> I want you to show love, not offer sacrifices. I want you to know me [God] more than I want burnt offerings. (Hos. 6:6 NLT)

> [Jesus] Then, calling the crowd to join his disciples, he said, "If any of you wants to be my follower, you must give up your own way, take up your cross, and follow me. If you try to hang on to your life, you will lose it. But if you give up your life for my sake and for the sake of the Good News, you will save it. And what do you benefit if you gain the whole world but lose your own soul?" (Mark 8:34–36 NLT)

I beseech you therefore, brethren, by the mercies of God, that you present your bodies a living sacrifice, holy, acceptable to God, *which is your* reasonable service. (Rom. 12:1 NKJV)

Tidbits & Morsels: Before the week is out, perform an anonymous act of kindness for the first person the Lord brings to your mind.

____

____

____

Sadness & Sorrow

How long will you forget me, Lord? Forever? How long will you look the other way when I am in need? How long must I be hiding daily anguish in my heart? How long shall my enemy have the upper hand? (Ps. 13:1–2 TLB)

All you saints! Sing your hearts out to God! Thank him to his face! He gets angry once in a while, but across a lifetime there is only love. The nights of crying your eyes out give way to days of laughter. (Ps. 30:4–5 MSG)

Why are you cast down, O my soul, and why are you in turmoil within me? Hope in God; for I shall again praise him, my salvation and my God. (Ps. 42:11 ESV)

Sorrow is better than laughter, for sadness has a refining influence on us. (Eccl. 7:3 NLT)

[Jesus] And he said to them, "My soul is crushed by sorrow to the point of death; stay here and watch with me." He went on a little farther and fell to the ground and prayed that if it were possible the awful hour awaiting him might never come. "Father, Father," he said, "everything is possible for you. Take away this cup from me. Yet I want your will, not mine." (Mark 14:34–36 TLB)

[Jesus] Very truly I tell you, you will weep and mourn while the world rejoices. You will grieve, but your grief will turn to joy. (John 16:20 NIV)

Tidbits & Morsels: Don't give up. Look up.

____

____

____

Say Grace

When you have eaten and are satisfied, praise the Lord your God for the good land he has given you. Be careful that you do not forget the Lord your God, failing to observe his commands, his laws and his decrees that I am giving you this day. Otherwise, when you eat and are satisfied, when you build fine houses and settle down, and when your herds and flocks grow large and your silver and gold increase and all you have is multiplied, then your heart will become proud and you will forget the Lord your God, who brought you out of Egypt, out of the land of slavery. (Deut. 8:10–14 NIV)

[Jesus] Then he had the people sit on the grass. He took the five loaves and two fish, lifted his face to heaven in prayer, blessed, broke, and gave the bread to the disciples. The disciples then gave the food to the congregation. They all ate their fill. (Matt. 14:19–20 MSG)

Just as day was dawning, Paul urged everyone [on board the ship] to eat. "You have been so worried that you haven't touched food for two weeks," he said. "Please eat something now for your own good. For not a hair of your heads will perish." Then he took some bread, gave thanks to God before them all, and broke off a piece and ate it. Then everyone was encouraged and began to eat—all 276 of us who were on board. (Acts 27:33–37 NLT)

They will say it is wrong to be married and wrong to eat meat, even though God gave these things to well-taught Christians to enjoy and be thankful for. For everything God made is good, and we may eat it gladly if we are thankful for it, and if we ask God to bless it, for it is made good by the Word of God and prayer. (1 Tim. 4:3–5 TLB)

Tidbits & Morsels: If it's not your usual practice to thank God before and/or after your meals, start today. If you do say grace, is it personal ... or by rote?

____

____

____

SEEK THE LORD

But from there you will seek the LORD your God and you will find him, if you search after him with all your heart and with all your soul. (Deut. 4:29 ESV)

Seek the LORD and his strength; seek his presence continually! (1 Chron. 16:11 ESV)

I love those who love me, and those who seek me diligently will find me. (Prov. 8:17 NKJV)

"If you look for me wholeheartedly, you will find me. I will be found by you," says the LORD. "I will end your captivity and restore your fortunes. I will gather you

> out of the nations where I sent you and will bring you home again to your own land." (Jer. 29:13–14 NLT)

> The Lord says to the people of Israel, "Seek me—and live." (Amos 5:4 TLB)

> [Jesus] Ask, and it will be given to you; seek, and you will find; knock, and it will be opened to you. For everyone who asks receives, and the one who seeks finds, and to the one who knocks it will be opened. Or which one of you, if his son asks him for bread, will give him a stone? Or if he asks for a fish, will give him a serpent? If you then, who are evil, know how to give good gifts to your children, how much more will your Father who is in heaven give good things to those who ask him! (Matt. 7:7–11 ESV)

Tidbits & Morsels: Place key Scripture verses on the refrigerator, inside cabinet doors, on the bathroom mirror, in the cookie jar—and switch them out often.

____

____

____

Self-centeredness or Selfishness

> My counsel is this: Live freely, animated and motivated by God's Spirit. Then you won't feed the compulsions of selfishness. For there is a root of sinful self-interest in us that is at odds with a free spirit, just as the free spirit is incompatible with selfishness. These two ways of life are contrary to each other, so that you cannot live at times one way and at times another way according to how you feel on any given day. Why don't you choose to be led by the Spirit and so escape the erratic compulsions of a law-dominated existence? It is obvious what kind of life develops out of trying to get

your own way all the time: repetitive, loveless, cheap sex; a stinking accumulation of mental and emotional garbage; frenzied and joyless grabs for happiness; trinket gods; magic-show religion; paranoid loneliness; cutthroat competition; all-consuming-yet-never-satisfied wants; a brutal temper; an impotence to love or be loved; divided homes and divided lives; small-minded and lopsided pursuits; the vicious habit of depersonalizing everyone into a rival; uncontrolled and uncontrollable addictions; ugly parodies of community. I could go on. (Gal. 5:16–21 MSG)

Do nothing from selfish ambition or conceit, but in humility count others more significant than yourselves. Let each of you look not only to his own interests, but also to the interests of others. (Phil. 2:3–4 ESV)

And by all means don't brag about being wise and good if you are bitter and jealous and selfish; that is the worst sort of lie. For jealousy and selfishness are not God's kind of wisdom. Such things are earthly, unspiritual, inspired by the devil. For wherever there is jealousy or selfish ambition, there will be disorder and every other kind of evil. (James 3:14–16 TLB)

Tidbits & Morsels: Do you help yourself first? And once your plate is full, do you cut up all your food to get a running head start? What are you, like five?

____

____

____

Self-condemnation

[Jesus] For God did not send His Son into the world to condemn the world, but that the world through

> Him might be saved. He who believes in Him is not condemned; but he who does not believe is condemned already, because he has not believed in the name of the only begotten Son of God. (John 3:17–18 NKJV)
>
> [Jesus] I tell you the truth, those who listen to my message and believe in God who sent me have eternal life. They will never be condemned for their sins, but they have already passed from death into life. (John 5:24 NLT)
>
> There is therefore now no condemnation to those who are in Christ Jesus, who do not walk according to the flesh, but according to the Spirit. For the law of the Spirit of life in Christ Jesus has made me free from the law of sin and death. For what the law could not do in that it was weak through the flesh, God did by sending His own Son in the likeness of sinful flesh, on account of sin: He condemned sin in the flesh, that the righteous requirement of the law might be fulfilled in us who do not walk according to the flesh but according to the Spirit. For those who live according to the flesh set their minds on the things of the flesh, but those who live according to the Spirit, the things of the Spirit. (Rom. 8:1–5 NKJV)
>
> By this we shall know that we are of the truth and reassure our heart before him; for whenever our heart condemns us, God is greater than our heart, and he knows everything. Beloved, if our heart does not condemn us, we have confidence before God. (1 John 3:19–21 ESV)

Tidbits & Morsels: Instead of berating yourself daily for mistakes you have made, keep a list of the things you've done right.

___

___

___

Self-control or Willpower

Like a city whose walls are broken through is a person who lacks self-control. (Prov. 25:28 NIV)

So he [the Angel of the Lord] answered and said to me: "This is the word of the Lord to Zerubbabel: 'Not by might nor by power, but by My Spirit,' says the Lord of hosts." (Zech. 4:6 NKJV)

[Jesus] The Spirit can make life. Sheer muscle and willpower don't make anything happen. (John 6:63 MSG)

But the fruit of the Spirit is love, joy, peace, patience, kindness, goodness, faithfulness, gentleness, self-control; against such things there is no law. And those who belong to Christ Jesus have crucified the flesh with its passions and desires. If we live by the Spirit, let us also keep in step with the Spirit. (Gal. 5:22–25 ESV)

But also for this very reason, giving all diligence, add to your faith virtue, to virtue knowledge, to knowledge self-control, to self-control perseverance, to perseverance godliness, to godliness brotherly kindness, and to brotherly kindness love. For if these things are yours and abound, you will be neither barren nor unfruitful in the knowledge of our Lord Jesus Christ. For he who lacks these things is shortsighted, even to blindness, and has forgotten that he was cleansed from his old sins. (2 Pet. 1:5–9 NKJV)

Tidbits & Morsels: If you wait too long to feed your hunger, it may gobble up your self-control.

____

____

____

Self-image & Self-worth

So God created man in His own image; in the image of God He created him; male and female He created them. (Gen. 1:27 NKJV)

For You formed my inward parts; You covered me in my mother's womb. I will praise You, for I am fearfully and wonderfully made; marvelous are Your works, and that my soul knows very well. My frame was not hidden from You, when I was made in secret, and skillfully wrought in the lowest parts of the earth. (Ps. 139:13–15 NKJV)

[Jesus] Are not five sparrows sold for two pennies? And not one of them is forgotten before God. Why, even the hairs of your head are all numbered. Fear not; you are of more value than many sparrows. (Luke 12:6–7 ESV)

Therefore, if anyone is in Christ, he is a new creation. The old has passed away; behold, the new has come. (2 Cor. 5:17 ESV)

But you are the ones chosen by God, chosen for the high calling of priestly work, chosen to be a holy people, God's instruments to do his work and speak out for him, to tell others of the night-and-day difference he made for you—from nothing to something, from rejected to accepted. (1 Pet. 2:9–10 MSG)

Tidbits & Morsels: Write down ten positive things about yourself.

____

____

____

Self-pity

God, God ... my God! Why did you dump me miles from nowhere? Doubled up with pain, I call to God all the day long. No answer. Nothing. I keep at it all night, tossing and turning. ... And here I am, a nothing—an earthworm, something to step on, to squash. Everyone pokes fun at me; they make faces at me, they shake their heads: "Let's see how God handles this one; since God likes him so much, let *him* help him!" (Ps. 22:1–2, 6–8 MSG)

And so God's people are dismayed and confused and drink it all in. "Does God realize what is going on?" they ask. "Look at these men of arrogance; they never have to lift a finger—theirs is a life of ease; and all the time their riches multiply." Have I been wasting my time? Why take the trouble to be pure? All I get out of it is trouble and woe—every day and all day long! (Ps. 73:10–14 TLB)

Who are the people who are always crying the blues? Who do you know who reeks of self-pity? Who keeps getting beaten up for no reason at all? Whose eyes are bleary and bloodshot? It's those who spend the night with a bottle, for whom drinking is serious business. (Prov. 23:29–31 MSG)

Cursed be the day in which I was born! Let the day not be blessed in which my mother bore me! Let the man be cursed who brought news to my father, saying, "A male child has been born to you!" making him very glad. And let that man be like the cities which the Lord overthrew and did not relent; let him hear the cry in the morning and the shouting at noon, because he did not kill me from the womb, that my mother might have been my grave, and her womb always enlarged with me. Why did I come forth from the womb to see labor and sorrow, that my days should be consumed with shame? (Jer. 20:14–18 NKJV)

Tidbits & Morsels: Remember, it's not always about you; it's always about Jesus.

Serve Others

> [Jesus] But Jesus called them to Himself and said to them, "You know that those who are considered rulers over the Gentiles lord it over them, and their great ones exercise authority over them. Yet it shall not be so among you; but whoever desires to become great among you shall be your servant. And whoever of you desires to be first shall be slave of all. For even the Son of Man did not come to be served, but to serve, and to give His life a ransom for many." (Mark 10:42–45 NKJV)
>
> [Jesus} So when He had washed their feet, taken His garments, and sat down again, He said to them, "Do you know what I have done to you? You call Me Teacher and Lord, and you say well, for so I am. If I then, your Lord and Teacher, have washed your feet, you also ought to wash one another's feet. For I have given you an example, that you should do as I have done to you. Most assuredly, I say to you, a servant is not greater than his master; nor is he who is sent greater than he who sent him. If you know these things, blessed are you if you do them. (John 13:12–17 NKJV)

Those of us who are strong and able in the faith need to step in and lend a hand to those who falter, and not just do what is most convenient for us. Strength is for service, not status. Each one of us needs to look after the good of the people around us, asking ourselves, "How can I help?" That's exactly what Jesus did. He didn't make it easy for himself by avoiding people's troubles but waded right in and helped out. (Rom. 15:1–3 MSG)

He comforts us in all our troubles so that we can comfort others. When they are troubled, we will be able to give them the same comfort God has given us. (2 Cor. 1:4 NLT)

Therefore, as we have opportunity, let us do good to all people, especially to those who belong to the family of believers. (Gal. 6:10 NIV)

For we are His workmanship, created in Christ Jesus for good works, which God prepared beforehand that we should walk in them. (Eph. 2:10 NKJV)

Each of you should use whatever gift you have received to serve others, as faithful stewards of God's grace in its various forms. (1 Pet. 4:10 NIV)

Tidbits & Morsels: Use your God-given talents to serve others in ways apart from dropping off another casserole.

____

____

____

Set Apart

But know that the Lord has set apart the godly for himself; the Lord hears when I call to him. (Ps. 4:3 ESV)

A life devoted to things is a dead life, a stump; a God-shaped life is a flourishing tree. (Prov. 11:28 MSG)

The Lord gave me [Jeremiah] this message: "I knew you before I formed you in your mother's womb. Before you were born, I set you apart and appointed you as my prophet to the nations." (Jer. 1:4–5 NLT)

> And now I [Paul] entrust you to God and his care and to his wonderful words that are able to build your faith and give you all the inheritance of those who are set apart for himself. (Acts 20:32 TLB)

> In a well-furnished kitchen there are not only crystal goblets and silver platters, but waste cans and compost buckets—some containers used to serve fine meals, others to take out the garbage. Become the kind of container God can use to present any and every kind of gift to his guests for their blessing. (2 Tim. 2:20–21 MSG)

Tidbits & Morsels: You are set apart by God. Now act like it!

____

____

____

Set Goals

> Don't continue doing things the way we're doing them at present, each of us doing as we wish. Until now you haven't arrived at the goal, the resting place, the inheritance that God, your God, is giving you. But the minute you cross the Jordan River and settle into the land God, your God, is enabling you to inherit, he'll give you rest from all your surrounding enemies. You'll be able to settle down and live in safety. (Deut. 12:8–10 MSG)

> Put God in charge of your work, then what you've planned will take place. (Prov. 16:3 MSG)

> Do your best, prepare for the worst—then trust God to bring victory. (Prov. 21:31 MSG)

> However, I [Paul] consider my life worth nothing to me; my only aim is to finish the race and complete the task the Lord Jesus has given me—the task of testifying to the good news of God's grace. (Acts 20:24 NIV)

> But one thing I [Paul] do: Forgetting what is behind and straining toward what is ahead, I press on toward the goal to win the prize for which God has called me (Phil. 3:13–14 NIV)

Tidbits & Morsels: Hurray! You've lost enough weight to wear your 20-year-old clothes, but should you ... really? [Wink.]

Shame

> Guard my life and rescue me; do not let me be put to shame for I take refuge in you. (Ps 25:20 NIV)

> Help me to love your every wish; then I will never have to be ashamed of myself. (Ps. 119:80 TLB)

> When wickedness comes, so does contempt, and with shame comes reproach. (Prov. 18:3 NIV)

> For the Scripture says, "Everyone who believes in him will not be put to shame." (Rom. 10:11 ESV)

> Remember, dear brothers and sisters, that few of you were wise in the world's eyes or powerful or wealthy when God called you. Instead, God chose things the world considers foolish in order to shame those who think they are wise. And he chose things that are powerless to shame those who are powerful. God chose things despised by the world, things counted as nothing at all, and used them to bring to nothing what the world considers important. (1 Cor. 1:26–28 NLT)

Tidbits & Morsels: With God's help, you can exchange embarrassment for motivation and shame for repentance.

____

____

____

Sin Nature

The Lord said to Cain, "Why are you angry, and why has your face fallen? If you do well, will you not be accepted? And if you do not do well, sin is crouching at the door. Its desire is contrary to you, but you must rule over it." (Gen. 4:6–7 ESV)

Keep your servant also from willful sins; may they not rule over me. Then will I be blameless, innocent of great transgression. (Ps. 19:13 NIV)

So the trouble is not with the law, for it is spiritual and good. The trouble is with me, for I am all too human, a slave to sin. I don't really understand myself, for I want to do what is right, but I don't do it. Instead, I do what I hate. But if I know that what I am doing is wrong, this shows that I agree that the law is good. So I am not the one doing wrong; it is sin living in me that does it. And I know that nothing good lives in me, that is, in my sinful nature. I want to do what is right, but I can't. I want to do what is good, but I don't. I don't want to do what is wrong, but I do it anyway. But if I do what I don't want to do, I am not really the one doing wrong; it is sin living in me that does it. I have discovered this principle of life—that when I want to do what is right, I inevitably do what is wrong. (Rom. 7:14–21 NLT)

Let us walk properly as in the daytime, not in orgies and drunkenness, not in sexual immorality and sensuality, not in quarreling and jealousy. But put on the Lord Jesus Christ, and make no provision for the flesh, to gratify its desires. (Rom. 13:13–14 ESV)

> If anyone, then, knows the good they ought to do and doesn't do it, it is sin for them. (James 4:17 NIV)

Tidbits & Morsels: When you slip (and you will) ask God to pick you up, put you back on the right path, and face you in the right direction.

____

____

____

Sleep

> I cried to the LORD with my voice, and He heard me from His holy hill. I lay down and slept; I awoke, for the LORD sustained me. (Ps. 3:4–5 NKJV)

> I will both lie down in peace, and sleep; for You alone, O LORD, make me dwell in safety. (Ps. 4:8 NKJV)

> Dear friend, guard Clear Thinking and Common Sense with your life; don't for a minute lose sight of them. ... You'll take afternoon naps without a worry, you'll enjoy a good night's sleep. (Prov. 3:21, 24 MSG)

> Love not sleep, lest you come to poverty; open your eyes, and you will have plenty of bread. (Prov. 20:13 ESV)

> The man who works hard sleeps well whether he eats little or much, but the rich must worry and suffer insomnia. (Eccl. 5:12 TLB)

Tidbits & Morsels: Tired? Grab a nap not a snack.

____

____

____

Soul

The law of the Lord is perfect, reviving the soul; the testimony of the Lord is sure, making wise the simple. (Ps. 19:7 ESV)

As the deer pants for streams of water, so my soul pants for you, my God. My soul thirsts for God, for the living God. When can I go and meet with God? (Ps. 42:1–2 NIV)

For He satisfies the longing soul, and fills the hungry soul with goodness. (Ps. 107:9 NKJV)

This is what the Lord says: "Stop at the crossroads and look around. Ask for the old, godly way, and walk in it. Travel its path, and you will find rest for your souls. But you reply, 'No, that's not the road we want!'" (Jer. 6:16 NLT)

[Jesus] For what will it profit a man if he gains the whole world and forfeits his soul? Or what shall a man give in return for his soul? (Matt. 16:26 ESV)

[Jesus] Your eyes light up your inward being. A pure eye lets sunshine into your soul. A lustful eye shuts out the light and plunges you into darkness. (Luke 11:34 TLB)

Tidbits & Morsels: Try to imagine the color of your soul. What color do you see?

____

____

____

Stay Alert

Just make sure you stay alert. Keep close watch over yourselves. Don't forget anything of what you've seen.

Don't let your heart wander off. Stay vigilant as long as you live. (Deut. 4:9 MSG)

[Jesus] But about that day or hour no one knows, not even the angels in heaven, nor the Son, but only the Father. Be on guard! Be alert! You do not know when that time will come. (Mark 13:32–33 NIV)

[Jesus] But watch yourselves lest your hearts be weighed down with dissipation and drunkenness and cares of this life, and that day come upon you suddenly like a trap. (Luke 21:34 ESV)

But friends, you're not in the dark, so how could you be taken off guard by any of this? You're sons of Light, daughters of Day. We live under wide open skies and know where we stand. So let's not sleepwalk through life like those others. Let's keep our eyes open and be smart. (1 Thess. 5:4–6 MSG)

Therefore, preparing your minds for action, and being sober-minded, set your hope fully on the grace that will be brought to you at the revelation of Jesus Christ. (1 Pet. 1:13 ESV)

Tidbits & Morsels: Be proactive. Flip the channel or mute the sound on all those fast-food commercials.

___

___

___

SUBMISSION

And it is good for people to submit at an early age to the yoke of his discipline. (Lam. 3:27 NLT)

[Jesus]: If anyone desires to come after Me, let him deny himself, and take up his cross daily, and follow Me. For whoever desires to save his life will lose it, but whoever loses his life for My sake will save it. (Luke 9:23–24 NKJV)

For the mind that is set on the flesh is hostile to God, for it does not submit to God's law; indeed, it cannot. (Rom. 8:7 ESV)

Honor Christ by submitting to each other. (Eph. 5:21 TLB)

Therefore submit to God. Resist the devil and he will flee from you. Draw near to God and He will draw near to you. Cleanse your hands, you sinners; and purify your hearts, you double-minded. Lament and mourn and weep! Let your laughter be turned to mourning and your joy to gloom. Humble yourselves in the sight of the Lord, and He will lift you up. (James 4:7–10 NKJV)

Tidbits & Morsels: Just because the package reads "single serving" doesn't mean you have to eat the contents in one sitting.

Success or Victory

The day my enemies turned tail and ran, they stumbled on you [God] and fell on their faces. You took over and set everything right; when I needed you, you were there, taking charge. (Ps. 9:3–4 MSG)

For it is you who light my lamp; the Lord my God lightens my darkness. For by you I can run against a troop, and by my God I can leap over a wall. (Ps. 18:28–29 ESV)

Give us aid against the enemy, for human help is worthless. With God we will gain the victory, and he will trample down our enemies. (Ps. 60:11–12 NIV)

My success—at which so many stand amazed—is because you are my mighty protector. (Ps. 71:7 TLB)

Do your best, prepare for the worst—then trust God to bring victory. (Prov. 21:31 MSG)

Do you not know that in a race all the runners run, but only one receives the prize? So run that you may obtain it. Every athlete exercises self-control in all things. They do it to receive a perishable wreath, but we an imperishable. So I do not run aimlessly; I do not box as one beating the air. But I discipline my body and keep it under control, lest after preaching to others I myself should be disqualified. (1 Cor. 9:24–27 ESV)

The sting of death is sin, and the strength of sin is the law. But thanks be to God, who gives us the victory through our Lord Jesus Christ. (1 Cor. 15:56–57 NKJV)

Tidbits & Morsels: Better to toss out good food than have good food go bad on your hips.

____

____

____

SURRENDER YOUR WILL (LET GO & LET GOD)

And Moses said to the people, "Do not be afraid. Stand still, and see the salvation of the LORD, which He will accomplish for you today. For the Egyptians whom you see today, you shall see again no more forever. The LORD will fight for you, and you shall hold your peace." (Ex. 14:13–14 NKJV)

> We can make our plans, but the final outcome is in God's hands. We can always "prove" that we are right, but is the Lord convinced? Commit your work to the Lord, then it will succeed. (Prov. 16:1–3 TLB)

> Although the Lord gives you the bread of adversity and the water of affliction, your teachers will be hidden no more; with your own eyes you will see them. Whether you turn to the right or to the left, your ears will hear a voice behind you, saying, "This is the way; walk in it." (Isa. 30:20–21 NIV)

> Don't worry about anything; instead, pray about everything; tell God your needs, and don't forget to thank him for his answers. If you do this, you will experience God's peace, which is far more wonderful than the human mind can understand. His peace will keep your thoughts and your hearts quiet and at rest as you trust in Christ Jesus. (Phil. 4:6–7 TLB)

> Submit yourselves therefore to God. Resist the devil, and he will flee from you. Draw near to God, and he will draw near to you. Cleanse your hands, you sinners, and purify your hearts, you double-minded. Be wretched and mourn and weep. Let your laughter be turned to mourning and your joy to gloom. Humble yourselves before the Lord, and he will exalt you. (James 4:7–10 ESV)

Tidbits & Morsels: Lift your arms, open your hands, and let God have your all!

____

____

____

Tell Others—As the Lord Prompts)

I proclaim your saving acts in the great assembly; I do not seal my lips, Lord, as you know. I do not hide your righteousness in my heart; I speak of your faithfulness and your saving help. I do not conceal your love and your faithfulness from the great assembly. (Ps. 40:9–10 NIV)

Rescue those who are being taken away to death; hold back those who are stumbling to the slaughter. If you say, "Behold, we did not know this," does not he who weighs the heart perceive it? Does not he who keeps watch over your soul know it, and will he not repay man according to his work? (Prov. 24:11–12 ESV)

[Jesus] Don't waste what is holy on people who are unholy. Don't throw your pearls to pigs! They will trample the pearls, then turn and attack you. (Matt. 7:6 NLT)

It's true that moral guidance and counsel need to be given, but the way you say it and to whom you say it are as important as what you say. (1 Tim. 1:8 MSG)

My dear friends, if you know people who have wandered off from God's truth, don't write them off. Go after them. Get them back and you will have rescued precious lives from destruction and prevented an epidemic of wandering away from God. (James 5:19–20 MSG)

But sanctify the Lord God in your hearts, and always be ready to give a defense to everyone who asks you a reason for the hope that is in you, with meekness and fear; having a good conscience, that when they defame you as evildoers, those who revile your good conduct in Christ may be ashamed. (1 Pet. 3:15–16 NKJV)

Tidbits & Morsels: Spend an hour with a friend, sharing positives, not negatives.

____

____

____

Temptation

[Jesus] Watch and pray so that you will not fall into temptation. The spirit is willing, but the flesh is weak. (Mark 14:38 NIV)

The temptations in your life are no different from what others experience. And God is faithful. He will not allow the temptation to be more than you can stand. When you are tempted, he will show you a way out so that you can endure. (1 Cor. 10:13 NLT)

Flee the evil desires of youth and pursue righteousness, faith, love, and peace, along with those who call on the Lord out of a pure heart. (2 Tim. 2:22 NIV)

For because he [Jesus] himself has suffered when tempted, he is able to help those who are being tempted. (Heb. 2:18 ESV)

Seeing then that we have a great High Priest who has passed through the heavens, Jesus the Son of God, let us hold fast our confession. For we do not have a High Priest who cannot sympathize with our weaknesses, but was in all points tempted as we are, yet without sin. (Heb. 4:14–15 NKJV)

And remember, when someone wants to do wrong it is never God who is tempting him, for God never wants to do wrong and never tempts anyone else to do it.

Temptation is the pull of man's own evil thoughts and wishes. These evil thoughts lead to evil actions and afterwards to the death penalty from God. (James 1:13–15 TLB)

Tidbits & Morsels: Plate your food at the stove. A dining table full of serving dishes can be tempting. Once your hunger is satisfied, push your plate away or put it in the sink.

____

____

____

Tests & Trials

But He knows the way that I take; when He has tested me, I shall come forth as gold. My foot has held fast to His steps; I have kept His way and not turned aside. I have not departed from the commandment of His lips; I have treasured the words of His mouth more than my necessary food. (Job 23:10–12 NKJV)

Oh, bless our God, you peoples! And make the voice of His praise to be heard, who keeps our soul among the living, and does not allow our feet to be moved. For You, O God, have tested us; You have refined us as silver is refined. You brought us into the net; You laid affliction on our backs. You have caused men to ride over our heads; we went through fire and through water; but You brought us out to rich fulfillment. (Ps. 66:8–12 NKJV)

Consider it a sheer gift, friends, when tests and challenges come at you from all sides. You know that under pressure, your faith-life is forced into the open and shows its true colors. So don't try to get out of anything prematurely. Let it do its work so you become mature and well-developed, not deficient in any way. ... Anyone who meets a testing challenge head-on and manages to stick it out is mighty fortunate. For such persons loyally in love with God, the reward is life and more life. (James 1:2–4, 12 MSG)

Dear friends, don't be surprised at the fiery trials you are going through, as if something strange were happening to you. Instead, be very glad—for these trials make you partners with Christ in his suffering, so that you will have the wonderful joy of seeing his glory when it is revealed to all the world. (1 Pet. 4:12–13 NLT)

Tidbits & Morsels: When you're at an event, position yourself as far away from the refreshment table as possible. And here's a novel concept: Not every meeting needs to have snacks.

____

____

____

Thankfulness

Oh give thanks to the LORD, for he is good; for his steadfast love endures forever! (1 Chron. 16:34 ESV)

Make thankfulness your sacrifice to God, and keep the vows you made to the Most High. (Ps. 50:14 NLT)

[Jesus] Then Jesus took the loaves, gave thanks to God, and distributed them to the people. Afterward he did the same with the fish. And they all ate as much as they wanted. (John 6:11 NLT)

Always give thanks for everything to our God and Father in the name of our Lord Jesus Christ. (Eph. 5:20 TLB)

Let the peace of Christ keep you in tune with each other, in step with each other. None of this going off and doing your own thing. And cultivate thankfulness. (Col. 3:15 MSG)

No matter what happens, always be thankful, for this is God's will for you who belong to Christ Jesus. (1 Thess. 5:18 TLB)

Tidbits & Morsels: What ten things are you most thankful for? Go!

____

____

____

Timing—God's, Not Yours

I will send my terror ahead of you and create panic among all the people whose lands you invade. I will make all your enemies turn and run. I will send terror ahead of you to drive out the Hivites, Canaanites, and Hittites. But I will not drive them out in a single year, because the land would become desolate and the wild animals would multiply and threaten you. I will drive them out a little at a time until your population has increased enough to take possession of the land. (Ex. 23:27–30 NLT)

At the set time that I appoint I will judge with equity. (Ps. 75:2 ESV)

Yet God has made everything beautiful for its own time. He has planted eternity in the human heart, but even so, people cannot see the whole scope of God's work from beginning to end. (Eccl. 3:11 NLT)

But these things I plan won't happen right away. Slowly, steadily, surely, the time approaches when the vision will be fulfilled. If it seems slow, do not despair, for these things will surely come to pass. Just be patient! They will not be overdue a single day! (Hab. 2:3 TLB)

When we were utterly helpless, with no way of escape, Christ came at just the right time and died for us sinners who had no use for him. (Rom. 5:6 TLB)

When is all this going to happen? I really don't need to say anything about that, dear brothers, for you know perfectly well that no one knows. That day of the Lord will come unexpectedly, like a thief in the night. (1 Thess. 5:1–2 TLB)

But do not overlook this one fact, beloved, that with the Lord one day is as a thousand years, and a thousand years as one day. (2 Pet. 3:8 ESV)

Tidbits & Morsels: Learn from yesterday, live for today, but plan for tomorrow.

____

____

____

TRUST

Some trust in chariots and some in horses, but we trust in the name of the LORD our God. (Ps. 20:7 ESV)

But when I am afraid, I will put my confidence in you. Yes, I will trust the promises of God. And since I am trusting him, what can mere man do to me? (Ps. 56:3–4 TLB)

Let the morning bring me word of your unfailing love, for I have put my trust in you. Show me the way I should go, for to you I entrust my life. (Ps. 143:8 NIV)

Trust in the LORD with all your heart; do not depend on your own understanding. Seek his will in all you do, and he will show you which path to take. Don't be impressed with your own wisdom. Instead, fear the LORD and turn away from evil. Then you will have healing for your body and strength for your bones. (Prov. 3:5–8 NLT)

Behold, God is my salvation; I will trust, and will not be afraid; for the LORD GOD is my strength and my song, and he has become my salvation. (Isa. 12:2 ESV)

[Jesus] Whoever can be trusted with very little can also be trusted with much, and whoever is dishonest with very little will also be dishonest with much. (Luke 16:10 NIV)

Tidbits & Morsels: Choose mentors you can trust, those who are both honest and encouraging.

____

____

____

WEAKNESS

He remembered our utter weakness, for his loving-kindness continues forever. (Ps. 136:23 TLB)

The law of Moses was unable to save us because of the weakness of our sinful nature. So God did what the law could not do. He sent his own Son in a body like the bodies we sinners have. And in that body God declared an end to sin's control over us by giving his Son as a sacrifice for our sins. (Rom. 8:3 NLT)

In the same way, the Spirit helps us in our weakness. We do not know what we ought to pray for, but the Spirit himself intercedes for us through wordless groans. (Rom. 8:26 NIV)

> I will say this: because these experiences I had were so tremendous, God was afraid I might be puffed up by them; so I was given a physical condition which has been a thorn in my flesh, a messenger from Satan to hurt and bother me and prick my pride. Three different times I begged God to make me well again. Each time he said, "No. But I am with you; that is all you need. My power shows up best in weak people." Now I am glad to boast about how weak I am; I am glad to be a living demonstration of Christ's power, instead of showing off my own power and abilities. Since I know it is all for Christ's good, I am quite happy about "the thorn," and about insults and hardships, persecutions and difficulties; for when I am weak, then I am strong—the less I have, the more I depend on him. (2 Cor. 12:7–10 TLB)

> This High Priest of ours understands our weaknesses since he had the same temptations we do, though he never once gave way to them and sinned. So let us come boldly to the very throne of God and stay there to receive his mercy and to find grace to help us in our times of need. (Heb. 4:15–16 TLB)

Tidbits & Morsels: Be thankful for your weaknesses for without them pride would take all the credit.

____

____

____

Wisdom

> You, through Your commandments, make me wiser than my enemies; for they are ever with me. I have more understanding than all my teachers, for Your testimonies are my meditation. I understand more than the ancients, because I keep Your precepts. I have restrained my feet from every evil way, that I may keep

> Your word. I have not departed from Your judgments, for You Yourself have taught me. How sweet are Your words to my taste, sweeter than honey to my mouth! Through Your precepts I get understanding; therefore I hate every false way. (Ps. 119:98–104 NKJV)

> For the Lord grants wisdom! His every word is a treasure of knowledge and understanding. He grants good sense to the godly—his saints. (Prov. 2:6–7 TLB)

> Wisdom has built her house; she has carved its seven columns. She has prepared a great banquet, mixed the wines, and set the table. She has sent her servants to invite everyone to come. She calls out from the heights overlooking the city. "Come in with me," she urges the simple. To those who lack good judgment, she says, "Come, eat my food, and drink the wine I have mixed. Leave your simple ways behind and begin to live; learn to use good judgment." (Prov. 9:1–6 NLT)

> But even so, the quiet words of a wise man are better than the shout of a king of fools. (Eccl. 9:17 TLB)

> Remember: The duller the ax the harder the work; use your head: The more brains, the less muscle. (Eccl. 10:10 MSG)

> If any of you lacks wisdom, let him ask of God, who gives to all liberally and without reproach, and it will be given to him. (James 1:5 NKJV)

> But the wisdom from above is first pure, then peaceable, gentle, open to reason, full of mercy and good fruits, impartial and sincere. (James 3:17 ESV)

Tidbits & Morsels: Though the psychology of yo-yo dieting baffles scientists, it does not baffle the God of all wisdom.

PART IV: THE GOD YOU SERVE

Since this field guide is ultimately about your relationship with the Lord rather than a list of diet rules, it's important that you know the God you serve. Here are just some of his attributes.

Abounding in Grace

For the sin of this one man, Adam, caused death to rule over many. But even greater is God's wonderful grace and his gift of righteousness, for all who receive it will live in triumph over sin and death through this one man, Jesus Christ. (Rom. 5:17 NLT)

In love he predestined us for adoption to sonship through Jesus Christ, in accordance with his pleasure and will—to the praise of his glorious grace, which he has freely given us in the One he loves. In him we have redemption through his blood, the forgiveness of sins, in accordance with the riches of God's grace that he lavished on us. (Eph. 1:4–8 NIV)

For the grace of God that brings salvation has appeared to all men, teaching us that, denying ungodliness and worldly lusts, we should live soberly, righteously, and godly in the present age, looking for the blessed hope and glorious appearing of our great God and Savior Jesus Christ, who gave Himself for us, that He might redeem us from every lawless deed and purify for Himself His own special people, zealous for good works. (Titus 2:11–14 NKJV)

Tidbits & Morsels: As God's grace operates, your part is to cooperate.

All-knowing

O Lord, you have examined my heart and know everything about me. You know when I sit or stand. When far away you know my every thought. You chart the path ahead of me and tell me where to stop and rest. Every moment you know where I am. You know what I am going to say before I even say it. You both precede and follow me and place your hand of blessing on my head. (Ps. 139:1–5 TLB)

Remember the things I have done in the past. For I alone am God! I am God, and there is none like me. Only I can tell you the future before it even happens. Everything I plan will come to pass, for I do whatever I wish. (Isa. 46:9–10 NLT)

And by this we know that we are of the truth, and shall assure our hearts before Him. For if our heart condemns us, God is greater than our heart, and knows all things. (1 John 3:19–20 NKJV

Tidbits & Morsels: God knows the 5 W's and 1 H of language: WHO you ate with, WHAT you ate, WHEN you ate, WHERE you ate, WHY you ate—and HOW much.

All-powerful & Almighty

Is anything too hard for the Lord? (Gen. 18:14 NIV)

Ah, Lord God! Behold, You have made the heavens and the earth by Your great power and outstretched arm. There is nothing too hard for You. ... Then the word of the Lord came to Jeremiah, saying, "Behold, I am the Lord, the God of all flesh. Is there anything too hard for Me?" (Jer. 32:17, 26–27 NKJV)

His coming is as brilliant as the sunrise. Rays of light flash from his hands, where his awesome power is hidden. (Hab. 3:4 NLT)

Tidbits & Morsels: God is stronger than any temptation the enemy can throw at you. And he's a much better catch too.

Comforter

When the cares of my heart are many, your consolations cheer my soul. (Ps. 94:19 ESV)

Blessed be the God and Father of our Lord Jesus Christ, the Father of mercies and God of all comfort, who comforts us in all our tribulation, that we may be able to comfort those who are in any trouble, with the comfort with which we ourselves are comforted by God. (2 Cor. 1:3–4 NKJV)

Now may our Lord Jesus Christ Himself, and our God and Father, who has loved us and given us everlasting consolation and good hope by grace, comfort your hearts and establish you in every good word and work. (2 Thess. 2:16–17 NKJV)

Tidbits & Morsels: Feelings come in fair weather and foul, but God's comfort does not waver.

____

____

____

Compassionate

And the Lord said, "I will cause all my goodness to pass in front of you, and I will proclaim my name, the Lord, in your presence. I will have mercy on whom I will have mercy, and I will have compassion on whom I will have compassion. (Ex. 33:19 NIV)

But you, O Lord, are a God merciful and gracious, slow to anger and abounding in steadfast love and faithfulness. (Ps. 86:15 ESV)

Though he [the Lord] brings grief, he also shows compassion because of the greatness of his unfailing love. (Lam. 3:32 NLT)

Where is another God like you, who pardons the guilt of the remnant, overlooking the sins of his special people? You will not stay angry with your people forever, because you delight in showing unfailing love. Once again you will have compassion on us. You will trample our sins under your feet and throw them into the depths of the ocean! (Mic. 7:18–19 NLT)

> [Jesus] Moved with compassion, Jesus reached out and touched him. "I am willing," he said. "Be healed!" (Mark 1:41 NLT)

> The Lord is full of compassion and mercy. (James 5:11 NIV)

Tidbits & Morsels: Have you known the compassion of the Lord? Well, good. Now pass it on to others.

____

____

____

Creator

> In the beginning, God created the heavens and the earth. (Gen. 1:1 ESV)

> God, your Redeemer, who shaped your life in your mother's womb, says: "I am God. I made all that is. With no help from you I spread out the skies and laid out the earth." (Isa. 44:24 MSG)

> For by Him all things were created that are in heaven and that are on earth, visible and invisible, whether thrones or dominions or principalities or powers. All things were created through Him and for Him. (Col. 1:16 NKJV)

Tidbits & Morsels: As you spend time in nature appreciating God's creation, you will experience a greater sense of his presence.

____

____

____

Deliverer & Protector

> I will love You, O Lord, my strength. The Lord is my rock and my fortress and my deliverer; my God, my strength, in whom I will trust; my shield and the horn of my salvation, my stronghold. (Ps. 18:1–2 NKJV)

> For the Lord God is a sun and shield; the Lord bestows favor and honor; no good thing does he withhold from those whose walk is blameless. (Ps 84:11 NIV)

> The Lord is good, a strong refuge when trouble comes. He is close to those who trust in him. (Nah. 1:7 NLT)

Tidbits & Morsels: Pray, and God will deliver you from turning to food. Ask, and he will protect you from overindulging.

____

____

____

Eternal & Infinite

> God said to Moses, "I am who I am. This is what you are to say to the Israelites: 'I am has sent me to you.'" (Ex. 3:14 NIV)

> Before the mountains were born or you brought forth the whole world, from everlasting to everlasting you are God. (Ps. 90:2 NIV)

> "I am the Alpha and the Omega," says the Lord God, "who is and who was and who is to come, the Almighty." (Rev. 1:8 ESV)

Tidbits & Morsels: Your eternal God promises you eternal life, which starts the moment you are born again!

____

____

____

Ever-present Everywhere

From heaven the Lord looks down and sees all mankind; from his dwelling place he watches all who live on earth—he who forms the hearts of all, who considers everything they do. (Ps. 33:13–15 NIV)

Where can I go from your Spirit? Where can I flee from your presence? If I go up to the heavens, you are there; if I make my bed in the depths, you are there. If I rise on the wings of the dawn, if I settle on the far side of the sea, even there your hand will guide me, your right hand will hold me fast. If I say, "Surely the darkness will hide me and the light become night around me," even the darkness will not be dark to you; the night will shine like the day, for darkness is as light to you. (Ps. 139:7–12 NIV)

The eyes of the Lord are in every place, keeping watch on the evil and the good. (Prov. 15:3 NKJV)

"Can anyone hide himself in secret places, so I shall not see him?" says the Lord; "Do I not fill heaven and earth?" says the Lord. (Jer. 23:24 NKJV)

Tidbits & Morsels: No matter where you go, there you are ... and so is God.

Exalted & Sovereign

Yours, O Lord, is the greatness and the power and the glory and the victory and the majesty, for all that is in the heavens and in the earth is yours. Yours is the kingdom, O Lord, and you are exalted as head above all. Both riches and honor come from you, and you rule over all. In your hand are power and might, and in your hand it is to make great and to give strength to all. And now we thank you, our God, and praise your glorious name. (1 Chron. 29:11–13 ESV)

He says, "Be still, and know that I am God; I will be exalted among the nations, I will be exalted in the earth." (Ps. 46:10 NIV)

All the glory of mankind will bow low; the pride of men will lie in the dust, and the Lord alone will be exalted. (Isa. 2:17 TLB)

Tidbits & Morsels: God is King of Kings, exalted above all! Don't bend your knee to another trendy diet god again.

Faithful

Know therefore that the Lord your God is God; he is the faithful God, keeping his covenant of love to a thousand generations of those who love him and keep his commandments. (Deut. 7:9 NIV)

O Jehovah, Commander of the heavenly armies, where is there any other Mighty One like you? Faithfulness is your very character. (Ps. 89:8 TLB)

Even when we are too weak to have any faith left, he remains faithful to us and will help us, for he cannot disown us who are part of himself, and he will always carry out his promises to us. (2 Tim. 2:13 TLB)

Tidbits & Morsels: Though your faith may falter, God's faith never does.

____

____

____

FATHER

And yet, O Lord, you are our Father. We are the clay and you are the Potter. We are all formed by your hand. (Isa. 64:8 TLB)

[Jesus] Now Jesus was praying in a certain place, and when he finished, one of his disciples said to him, "Lord, teach us to pray, as John taught his disciples." And he said to them, "When you pray, say: 'Father, hallowed be your name.'" (Luke 11:1–2 ESV)

The Spirit you received does not make you slaves, so that you live in fear again; rather, the Spirit you received brought about your adoption to sonship. And by him we cry, "*Abba*, Father." The Spirit himself testifies with our spirit that we are God's children. Now if we are children, then we are heirs—heirs of God and co-heirs with Christ, if indeed we share in his sufferings in order that we may also share in his glory. (Rom. 8:15–17 NIV)

Tidbits & Morsels: God, the only perfect Father, is longing for you to sit at his feet and confide in him.

Feared & Revered

> For who in all of heaven can be compared with God? What mightiest angel is anything like him? The highest of angelic powers stand in dread and awe of him. Who is as revered as he by those surrounding him? (Ps. 89:6–7 TLB)

> For the LORD spoke thus to me with his strong hand upon me, and warned me not to walk in the way of this people, saying: "Do not call conspiracy all that this people calls conspiracy, and do not fear what they fear, nor be in dread. But the LORD of hosts, him you shall honor as holy. Let him be your fear, and let him be your dread." (Isa. 8:11–13 ESV)

> The purpose of my [the LORD's] covenant with the Levites was to bring life and peace, and that is what I gave them. This required reverence from them, and they greatly revered me and stood in awe of my name. (Mal. 2:5 NLT)

Tidbits & Morsels: You don't fear and revere God because he is scary; you do so because he is holy.

Forgiving

Then if my people who are called by my name will humble themselves and pray and seek my face and turn from their wicked ways, I will hear from heaven and will forgive their sins and restore their land. (2 Chron. 7:14 NLT)

He never bears a grudge, nor remains angry forever. He has not punished us as we deserve for all our sins, for his mercy toward those who fear and honor him is as great as the height of the heavens above the earth. He has removed our sins as far away from us as the east is from the west. (Ps. 103:9–12 TLB)

Who is a God like you, pardoning iniquity and passing over transgression for the remnant of his inheritance? He does not retain his anger forever, because he delights in steadfast love. He will again have compassion on us; he will tread our iniquities underfoot. You will cast all our sins into the depths of the sea. (Mic. 7:18–19 ESV)

Tidbits & Morsels: To forgive the way the Lord forgives, you must forget the offense. Are you willing?

____

____

____

Glorious

I am the Lord; that is my name; my glory I give to no other, nor my praise to carved idols. (Isa. 42:8 ESV)

[Jesus] Now the Son of Man is seen for who he is, and God seen for who he is in him. The moment God is seen in him, God's glory will be on display. In glorifying him, he himself is glorified—glory all around! (John 13:31–32 MSG)

All glory to him who alone is God, our Savior through Jesus Christ our Lord. All glory, majesty, power, and authority are his before all time, and in the present, and beyond all time! Amen. (Jude 25 NLT)

Tidbits & Morsels: There is no way you can fully wrap your mind around the glorious God you serve! And aren't you glad?

____

____

____

Good

Good and upright is the Lord; therefore he instructs sinners in his ways. (Ps. 25:8 NIV)

Oh, taste and see that the Lord is good! (Ps. 34:8 ESV)

You are good and You do good; teach me Your statutes. (Ps. 119:67–68 ESV)

Tidbits & Morsels: God's goodness is pure through and through.

____

____

____

Head of the Church

God has put all things under the authority of Christ and has made him head over all things for the benefit of the church. And the church is his body; it is made full and complete by Christ, who fills all things everywhere with himself. (Eph. 1:22–23 NLT)

And he [Christ] is the head of the body, the church. He is the beginning, the firstborn from the dead, that in everything he might be preeminent. (Col. 1:18 ESV)

Now that we know what we have—Jesus, this great High Priest with ready access to God—let's not let it slip through our fingers. We don't have a priest who is out of touch with our reality. He's been through weakness and testing, experienced it all—all but the sin. (Heb. 4:14–15 MSG)

Tidbits & Morsels: Jesus is your senior pastor. He has all the time you'll ever need in his schedule.

____

____

____

HEALER

There the LORD made for them a statute and a rule, and there he tested them, saying, "If you will diligently listen to the voice of the LORD your God, and do that which is right in his eyes, and give ear to his commandments and keep all his statutes, I will put none of the diseases on you that I put on the Egyptians, for I am the LORD, your healer." (Ex. 15:25–26 ESV)

Praise the LORD, my soul; all my inmost being, praise his holy name. Praise the LORD, my soul, and forget not all his benefits—who forgives all your sins and heals all your diseases. (Ps. 103:1–3 NIV)

> He heals the brokenhearted and bandages their wounds. (Ps. 147:3 NLT)

Tidbits & Morsels: The Lord is able to heal your mind, spirit, soul, and body.

____

____

____

Helper

> It is the Lord who goes before you. He will be with you; he will not leave you or forsake you. Do not fear or be dismayed. (Deut. 31:8 ESV)

> For the eyes of the Lord search back and forth across the whole earth, looking for people whose hearts are perfect toward him, so that he can show his great power in helping them. (2 Chron. 16:9 TLB)

> I lift up my eyes to the mountains—where does my help come from? My help comes from the Lord, the Maker of heaven and earth. He will not let your foot slip—he who watches over you will not slumber; indeed, he who watches over Israel will neither slumber nor sleep. The Lord watches over you—the Lord is your shade at your right hand; the sun will not harm you by day, nor the moon by night. The Lord will keep you from all harm—he will watch over your life; the Lord will watch over your coming and going both now and forevermore. (Ps. 121:1–8 NIV)

Tidbits & Morsels: The Holy Spirit helps you with all things, big and small. All you have to do is ask.

Holy

Who is like you, O Lord, among the gods? Who is like you, majestic in holiness, awesome in glorious deeds, doing wonders? (Ex. 15:11 ESV)

I am the Lord your God; consecrate yourselves and be holy because I am holy. (Lev. 11:44 NIV)

And the four living creatures, each of them with six wings, are full of eyes all around and within, and day and night they never cease to say, "Holy, holy, holy, is the Lord God Almighty, who was and is and is to come!" (Rev. 4:8 NKJV)

Tidbits & Morsels: God is and always has been without sin.

Incomparable & Transcendent

Therefore, you are great, O Lord God. For there is none like you, and there is no God besides you, according to all that we have heard with our ears. (2 Sam. 7:22 ESV)

The one thing I want from God, the thing I seek most of all, is the privilege of meditating in his Temple, living in his presence every day of my life, delighting in his incomparable perfections and glory. (Ps. 27:4 TLB)

> So to whom will you compare me, the Incomparable? Can you picture me without reducing me?" ... I am God, the only God you've had or ever will have—incomparable, irreplaceable— (Isa. 46:5, 9 MSG)

Tidbits & Morsels: Be reasonable. There is no comparison between your small sacrifices and those of Jesus, or between your flawed virtues and the perfection of God.

___

___

___

Jealous

> You shall not make for yourself a carved image—any likeness of anything that is in heaven above, or that is in the earth beneath, or that is in the water under the earth; you shall not bow down to them nor serve them. For I, the Lord your God, am a jealous God, visiting the iniquity of the fathers upon the children to the third and fourth generations of those who hate Me, but showing mercy to thousands, to those who love Me and keep My commandments. (Ex. 20:4–6 NKJV)

> So stay alert. Don't for a minute forget the covenant which God, your God, made with you. And don't take up with any carved images, no forms of any kind—God, your God, issued clear commands on that. God, your God, is not to be trifled with—he's a consuming fire, a jealous God. (Deut. 4:23–24 MSG)

> God is jealous over those he loves; that is why he takes vengeance on those who hurt them. He furiously destroys their enemies. (Nah. 1:2 TLB)

Tidbits & Morsels: God's jealousy for you simply means God wants nothing but the best for you—him!

Jesus

> The next day he [John the Baptist] saw Jesus coming toward him, and said, "Behold, the Lamb of God, who takes away the sin of the world!" (John 1:29 ESV)

> But these are written that you may believe that Jesus is the Messiah, the Son of God, and that by believing you may have life in his name. (John 20:31 NIV)

> He [Jesus] is the image of the invisible God, the firstborn of all creation. (Col. 1:15 ESV)

> And we have seen and testify that the Father has sent the Son as Savior of the world. (1 John 4:14 NKJV)

> And we know that Christ, God's Son, has come to help us understand and find the true God. And now we are in God because we are in Jesus Christ his Son, who is the only true God; and he is eternal Life. (1 John 5:20 TLB)

Tidbits & Morsels: Son of God and Savior of the world—which includes you!

JUST

> The Rock, his work is perfect, for all his ways are justice. A God of faithfulness and without iniquity, just and upright is he. (Deut. 32:4 ESV)

> [Jesus] And the Lord said, "Hear what the unrighteous judge says. And will not God give justice to his elect, who cry to him day and night? Will he delay long over them?" (Luke 18:6–7 ESV)

> [Jesus] I can do nothing on my own. I judge as God tells me. Therefore, my judgment is just, because I carry out the will of the one who sent me, not my own will. (John 5:30 NLT)

Tidbits & Morsels: God can only behave according to what is morally right. His justice and word does not waver with the opinions or whims of the diet industry.

____

____

____

LORD OF ALL

> For the LORD your God is God of gods and Lord of lords, the great, the mighty, and the awesome God, who is not partial and takes no bribe. (Deut. 10:17 ESV)

> I am the LORD, and there is no other; there is no God besides Me. I will gird you, though you have not known Me, that they may know from the rising of the sun to its setting that there is none besides Me. I am the LORD, and there is no other; I form the light and create darkness, I make peace and create calamity; I, the LORD, do all these things. (Isa. 45:5–7 NKJV)

For at just the right time Christ will be revealed from heaven by the blessed and only almighty God, the King of all kings and Lord of all lords. (1 Tim. 6:15 NLT)

Tidbits & Morsels: When you accept Jesus as your personal Savior and crown him Lord of your life, everything you do—and everything you eat—is subject to his authority.

___

___

___

Love & Loving

[Jesus] For this is how God loved the world: He gave his one and only Son, so that everyone who believes in him will not perish but have eternal life. God sent his Son into the world not to judge the world, but to save the world through him. (John 3:16–17 NLT)

For I am convinced that nothing can ever separate us from his love. Death can't, and life can't. The angels won't, and all the powers of hell itself cannot keep God's love away. Our fears for today, our worries about tomorrow, or where we are—high above the sky, or in the deepest ocean—nothing will ever be able to separate us from the love of God demonstrated by our Lord Jesus Christ when he died for us. (Rom. 8:38–39 TLB)

Beloved, let us love one another, for love is of God; and everyone who loves is born of God and knows God. He who does not love does not know God, for God is love. In this the love of God was manifested toward us, that God has sent His only begotten Son into the world, that we might live through Him. In this is love, not that we loved God, but that He loved us and sent His Son to be the propitiation for our sins. Beloved, if

> God so loved us, we also ought to love one another. (1 John 4:7–12 NKJV)

Tidbits & Morsels: You ask: "God, how can you love me after what I did?" God answers, "How? I will die for you." And then he did.

____

____

____

Merciful

> Oh, taste and see that the Lord is good; blessed is the man who trusts in Him! (Ps. 34:8 NKJV)

> The faithful love of the Lord never ends! His mercies never cease. Great is his faithfulness; his mercies begin afresh each morning. (Lam. 3:22–23 NLT)

> For he [God] says to Moses, "I will have mercy on whom I have mercy, and I will have compassion on whom I have compassion." So then it depends not on human will or exertion, but on God, who has mercy. (Rom. 9:15–16 ESV)

Tidbits & Morsels: God's mercies are new every morning ... and before and after every meal.

____

____

____

Patient & Longsuffering

> For many years you were patient with them. By your Spirit you warned them through your prophets. Yet they

paid no attention, so you gave them into the hands of the neighboring peoples. (Neh. 9:30 NIV)

But I received mercy for this reason, that in me, as the foremost, Jesus Christ might display his perfect patience as an example to those who were to believe in him for eternal life. (1 Tim. 1:16 ESV)

The Lord isn't really being slow about his promise, as some people think. No, he is being patient for your sake. He does not want anyone to be destroyed, but wants everyone to repent. (2 Pet. 3:9 NLT)

Tidbits & Morsels: God's patience can outlast yours. Just you wait ...

____

____

____

Praiseworthy

For great is the LORD and most worthy of praise; he is to be feared above all gods. (1 Chron. 16:25 NIV)

Praise the LORD! Praise, O servants of the LORD, praise the name of the LORD! Blessed be the name of the LORD from this time forth and forevermore! From the rising of the sun to its setting, the name of the LORD is to be praised! (Ps. 113:1–3 ESV)

And whenever the living creatures give glory and honor and thanks to him who is seated on the throne, who lives forever and ever, the twenty-four elders fall down before him who is seated on the throne and worship him who lives forever and ever. They cast their crowns before the throne, saying, "Worthy are you, our Lord and God, to receive glory and honor and power, for you

> created all things, and by your will they existed and were created." (Rev. 4:9–11 ESV)

Tidbits & Morsels: Praise God for the freedom he's given you to enjoy choice meals and good fellowship.

____

____

____

Promise Keeper

> Not one word of all the good promises that the Lord had made to the house of Israel had failed; all came to pass. (Josh. 21:45 ESV)

> For no matter how many promises God has made, they are "Yes" in Christ. And so through him the "Amen" is spoken by us to the glory of God. (2 Cor. 1:20 NIV)

> What agreement has the temple of God with idols? For we are the temple of the living God; as God said, "I will make my dwelling among them and walk among them, and I will be their God, and they shall be my people. Therefore go out from their midst, and be separate from them, says the Lord, and touch no unclean thing; then I will welcome you, and I will be a father to you, and you shall be sons and daughters to me, says the Lord Almighty." ... Since we have these promises, beloved, let us cleanse ourselves from every defilement of body and spirit, bringing holiness to completion in the fear of God. (2 Cor. 6:16–18, 7:1 ESV)

Tidbits & Morsels: God cannot lie. If he says he will do something, he will do it.

Provider

For it was I, Jehovah your God, who brought you out of the land of Egypt. Only test me! Open your mouth wide and see if I won't fill it. You will receive every blessing you can use! (Ps. 81:10 TLB)

He who did not spare his own Son but gave him up for us all, how will he not also with him graciously give us all things? (Rom. 8:32 ESV)

And my God shall supply all your need according to His riches in glory by Christ Jesus. (Phil. 4:19 NKJV)

Tidbits & Morsels: The Lord provides all your needs, even those you don't know about yet.

Righteous

Lord, the God of Israel, you are righteous! (Ezra 9:15 NIV)

Your righteousness, God, reaches to the heavens, you who have done great things. Who is like you, God? (Ps. 71:19 NIV)

God presented Christ as a sacrifice of atonement, through the shedding of his blood—to be received by faith. He did this to demonstrate his righteousness, because in his forbearance he had left the sins committed

> beforehand unpunished—he did it to demonstrate his righteousness at the present time, so as to be just and the one who justifies those who have faith in Jesus. (Rom. 3:25–26 NIV)

Tidbits & Morsels: As a born-again believer, you are righteous in Christ—not in what you eat or don't eat.

Savior & Redeemer

> Blessed be the Lord—day after day he carries us along. He's our Savior, our God, oh yes! He's God-for-us, he's God-who-saves-us. (Ps. 68:19–20 MSG)

> Fear not, you worm Jacob, you men of Israel! I am the one who helps you, declares the Lord; your Redeemer is the Holy One of Israel. (Isa. 41:14 ESV)

> That night there were shepherds staying in the fields nearby, guarding their flocks of sheep. Suddenly, an angel of the Lord appeared among them, and the radiance of the Lord's glory surrounded them. They were terrified, but the angel reassured them. "Don't be afraid!" he said. "I bring you good news that will bring great joy to all people. The Savior—yes, the Messiah, the Lord has been born today in Bethlehem, the city of David!" (Luke 2:8–11 NLT)

Tidbits & Morsels: Jesus Christ has redeemed you from a life of sin! You "being good" by following a diet has nothing to do with it. Redemption is by Christ alone!

Self-sufficient

The earth belongs to God! Everything in all the world is his! (Ps. 24:1 TLB)

Listen, my people, and I will speak; I will testify against you, Israel: I am God, your God. I bring no charges against you concerning your sacrifices or concerning your burnt offerings, which are ever before me. I have no need of a bull from your stall or of goats from your pens, for every animal of the forest is mine, and the cattle on a thousand hills. I know every bird in the mountains, and the insects in the fields are mine. If I were hungry I would not tell you, for the world is mine, and all that is in it. (Ps. 50:7–12 NIV)

God, who made the world and everything in it, since He is Lord of heaven and earth, does not dwell in temples made with hands. Nor is He worshiped with men's hands, as though He needed anything, since He gives to all life, breath, and all things. And He has made from one blood every nation of men to dwell on all the face of the earth, and has determined their preappointed times and the boundaries of their dwellings, so that they should seek the Lord, in the hope that they might grope for Him and find Him, though He is not far from each one of us. (Acts 17:24–27 NKJV)

Tidbits & Morsels: Don't mistake your independent spirit with God's self-sufficiency. You can do nothing well apart from him.

Spirit

The earth was without form and void, and darkness was over the face of the deep. And the Spirit of God was hovering over the face of the waters. (Gen. 1:2 ESV)

The Spirit of God has made me; the breath of the Almighty gives me life. (Job 33:4 NIV)

A shoot will come up from the stump of Jesse; from his roots a Branch will bear fruit. The Spirit of the Lord will rest on him—the Spirit of wisdom and of understanding, the Spirit of counsel and of might, the Spirit of the knowledge and fear of the Lord—and he will delight in the fear of the Lord. (Isa. 11:1–3 NIV)

Tidbits & Morsels: God is Spirit and Holy. Satan is spirit but unholy. Stay alert!

____

____

____

Sustainer

You sent your good Spirit to instruct them, and you did not stop giving them manna from heaven or water for their thirst. For forty years you sustained them in the wilderness, and they lacked nothing. Their clothes did not wear out, and their feet did not swell! (Neh. 9:20–21 NLT)

Even to your old age and gray hairs I am he, I am he who will sustain you. I have made you and I will carry you; I will sustain you and I will rescue you. (Isa. 46:4 NIV)

Your words are what sustain me; they are food to my hungry soul. They bring joy to my sorrowing heart and delight me. How proud I am to bear your name, O Lord. (Jer. 15:16 TLB)

Tidbits & Morsels: God encourages you to lean on him and to rest in him. He upholds you in good times and bad.

____

____

____

Triune

[Jesus] And Jesus came and said to them, "All authority in heaven and on earth has been given to me. Go therefore and make disciples of all nations, baptizing them in the name of the Father and of the Son and of the Holy Spirit, teaching them to observe all that I have commanded you." (Matt. 28:18–20 ESV)

[Jesus] But when the Father sends the Advocate as my representative—that is, the Holy Spirit—he will teach you everything and will remind you of everything I have told you. (John 14:26 NLT)

Now all of us can come to the Father through the same Holy Spirit because of what Christ has done for us. (Eph. 2:18 NLT)

Tidbits & Morsels: Father, Son, and Holy Spirit are for you, not against you.

____

____

____

Trustworthy

God is not human, that he should lie, not a human being, that he should change his mind. Does he speak and then not act? Does he promise and not fulfill? (Num. 23:19 NIV)

The works of his hands are faithful and just; all his precepts are trustworthy; they are established forever and ever, to be performed with faithfulness and uprightness. (Ps. 111:7–8 ESV)

The Lord is trustworthy in all he promises and faithful in all he does. (Ps. 145:13 NIV)

Tidbits & Morsels: You can trust God and his Word ... when you know God and read his Word.

____

____

____

Truth

What you say goes, God, and stays, as permanent as the heavens. Your truth never goes out of fashion; it's as relevant as the earth when the sun comes up. Your Word and truth are dependable as ever; that's what you ordered—you set the earth going. (Ps. 119:89–91 MSG)

[Jesus] I am the way, and the truth, and the life. No one comes to the Father except through me. (John 14:6 ESV)

[Jesus] When the Advocate comes, whom I will send to you from the Father—the Spirit of truth who goes out from the Father—he will testify about me. (John 15:26 NIV)

Tidbits & Morsels: Unlike diet gurus and marketing sharks, God never lies. Unlike well-meaning health professionals, God never makes mistakes.

UNCHANGING

I am the LORD, and I do not change. (Mal. 3:6 NLT)

Jesus Christ is the same yesterday, today, and forever. (Heb. 13:8 NKJV)

Every good gift and every perfect gift is from above, coming down from the Father of lights with whom there is no variation or shadow due to change. (James 1:17 ESV)

Tidbits & Morsels: God and his Word do not change with the whims and ways of the world—or the diet industry.

WISDOM & WISE

The Lord's wisdom founded the earth; his understanding established all the universe and space. The deep fountains of the earth were broken open by his knowledge, and the skies poured down rain. (Prov. 3:19–20 TLB)

> He will be the sure foundation for your times, a rich store of salvation and wisdom and knowledge; the fear of the LORD is the key to this treasure. (Isa. 33:6 NIV)

> Have you ever come on anything quite like this extravagant generosity of God, this deep, deep wisdom? It's way over our heads. We'll never figure it out. Is there anyone around who can explain God? Anyone smart enough to tell him what to do? Anyone who has done him such a huge favor that God has to ask his advice? Everything comes from him; everything happens through him; everything ends up in him. (Rom. 11:33–35 MSG)

Tidbits & Morsels: God's wisdom will lead you to the type of food your body needs. Unwise choices are all on you.

____

____

____

WORD, THE

> In the beginning was the Word, and the Word was with God, and the Word was God. He was with God in the beginning. Through him all things were made; without him nothing was made that has been made. (John 1:1–3 NIV)

> For whatever God says to us is full of living power: it is sharper than the sharpest dagger, cutting swift and deep into our innermost thoughts and desires with all their parts, exposing us for what we really are. (Heb. 4:12 TLB)

> Now I saw heaven opened, and behold, a white horse. And He who sat on him was called Faithful and True, and in righteousness He judges and makes war. His eyes were like a flame of fire, and on His head were

> many crowns. He had a name written that no one knew except Himself. He was clothed with a robe dipped in blood, and His name is called The Word of God. (Rev. 19:11–13 NKJV)

Tidbits & Morsels: Dine on God's Word daily to be transformed daily!

WRATH

> For thus says the High and Lofty One who inhabits eternity, whose name is Holy: "I dwell in the high and holy place, with him who has a contrite and humble spirit, to revive the spirit of the humble, and to revive the heart of the contrite ones. For I will not contend forever, nor will I always be angry; for the spirit would fail before Me, and the souls which I have made." (Isa. 57:15–16 NKJV)

> Your silver and gold will be of no use to you in that day of the Lord's wrath. You cannot ransom yourselves with it. For the whole land will be devoured by the fire of his jealousy. (Zeph. 1:18 TLB)

> For the wrath of God is revealed from heaven against all ungodliness and unrighteousness of men, who by their unrighteousness suppress the truth. (Rom. 1:18 ESV)

Tidbits & Morsels: To escape the wrath of God—which will come—accept Jesus as your Lord and Savior.

PART V: WHAT GOD SAYS ABOUT YOU

Take heart! What God says about you is more accurate, balanced, grace-filled, and merciful than what you say or think about yourself.

ADOPTED

> You can tell for sure that you are now fully adopted as his own children because God sent the Spirit of his Son into our lives crying out, "Papa! Father!" Doesn't that privilege of intimate conversation with God make it plain that you are not a slave, but a child? And if you are a child, you're also an heir, with complete access to the inheritance. (Gal. 4:6–7 MSG)
>
> His [God's] unchanging plan has always been to adopt us into his own family by sending Jesus Christ to die for us. And he did this because he wanted to! (Eph. 1:5 TLB)

Tidbits & Morsels: Children adopted into the family of God are so loved!

____

____

____

Alive in Christ

> For as in Adam all die, even so in Christ all shall be made alive. (1 Cor. 15:22 NKJV)

> But God, who is rich in mercy, because of His great love with which He loved us, even when we were dead in trespasses, made us alive together with Christ (by grace you have been saved) ... (Eph. 2:4–5 NKJV)

Tidbits & Morsels: Being alive in Christ doesn't mean your life will match all your happy social media posts. Being alive in Christ means you have a strong foundation to help you weather life's storms.

____

____

____

Branch of the True Vine

> [Jesus] I am the vine; you are the branches. If you remain in me and I in you, you will bear much fruit; apart from me you can do nothing. If you do not remain in me, you are like a branch that is thrown away and withers; such branches are picked up, thrown into the fire and burned. If you remain in me and my words remain in you, ask whatever you wish, and it will be done for you. This is to my Father's glory, that you bear much fruit, showing yourselves to be my disciples. (John 15:5–8 NIV)

Tidbits & Morsels: The vine (the Lord) pumps life into each branch (you), so each branch can produce fruit.

____

____

____

Child of God

> But to all who did receive him, who believed in his name, he gave the right to become children of God, who were born, not of blood nor of the will of the flesh nor of the will of man, but of God. (John 1:12–13 ESV)
>
> Behold what manner of love the Father has bestowed on us, that we should be called children of God! Therefore the world does not know us, because it did not know Him. (1 John 3:1 NKJV)

Tidbits & Morsels: You are a child of God. So am I. We are all God's favorites, so there's no reason for sibling rivalry.

____

____

____

Chosen

> Do this because you are a people set apart as holy to God, your God. God, your God, chose you out of all the people on Earth for himself as a cherished, personal treasure. (Deut. 7:6 MSG)
>
> Long ago, even before he made the world, God chose us to be his very own through what Christ would do for us; he decided then to make us holy in his eyes, without a single fault—we who stand before him covered with his love. (Eph. 1:4 TLB)

Tidbits & Morsels: Long before you even knew God, he chose you.

____

____

____

Citizen of Heaven

> But our citizenship is in heaven, and from it we await a Savior, the Lord Jesus Christ, who will transform our lowly body to be like his glorious body, by the power that enables him even to subject all things to himself. (Phil. 3:20–21 ESV)

> Each one of these people of faith died not yet having in hand what was promised, but still believing. How did they do it? They saw it way off in the distance, waved their greeting, and accepted the fact that they were transients in this world. People who live this way make it plain that they are looking for their true home. If they were homesick for the old country, they could have gone back any time they wanted. But they were after a far better country than that—heaven country. You can see why God is so proud of them, and has a City waiting for them. (Heb. 11:13–16 MSG)

Tidbits & Morsels: You may claim an earthly nationality, but you are actually a citizen of heaven.

____

____

____

Complete in Christ

> Therefore, if anyone is in Christ, he is a new creation; old things have passed away; behold, all things have become new. (2 Cor. 5:17 NKJV)

> You don't need a telescope, a microscope, or a horoscope to realize the fullness of Christ, and the emptiness of the universe without him. When you come to him, that fullness comes together for you, too. His power extends over everything. (Col. 2:9–10 MSG)

Tidbits & Morsels: We are nothing apart from Christ. In Christ, we are whole.

Fellow Heir with Christ

The Spirit himself bears witness with our spirit that we are children of God, and if children, then heirs—heirs of God and fellow heirs with Christ, provided we suffer with him in order that we may also be glorified with him. (Rom. 8:16–17 ESV)

But when the kindness and love of God our Savior appeared, he saved us, not because of righteous things we had done, but because of his mercy. He saved us through the washing of rebirth and renewal by the Holy Spirit, whom he poured out on us generously through Jesus Christ our Savior, so that, having been justified by his grace, we might become heirs having the hope of eternal life. (Titus 3:4–7 NIV)

Tidbits & Morsels: Because we are one with Christ, we inherit what Christ inherits. Heaven!

Forgiven & Redeemed

In him we have redemption through his blood, the forgiveness of sins, in accordance with the riches of God's grace that he lavished on us. (Eph. 1:7–8 NIV)

> But if we confess our sins to him, he can be depended on to forgive us and to cleanse us from every wrong. And it is perfectly proper for God to do this for us because Christ died to wash away our sins. (1 John 1:9 TLB)

Tidbits & Morsels: Jesus died to pay the full price for your sins and saved you from the pit of hell.

____

____

____

Friend of Jesus

> [Jesus] Greater love has no one than this, that someone lay down his life for his friends. You are my friends if you do what I command you. No longer do I call you servants, for the servant does not know what his master is doing; but I have called you friends, for all that I have heard from my Father I have made known to you. (John 15:13–15 ESV)

> For since our friendship with God was restored by the death of his Son while we were still his enemies, we will certainly be saved through the life of his Son. (Rom. 5:10 NLT)

Tidbits & Morsels: Jesus is the closest friend you'll ever have. Share your deepest thoughts with him and listen for his response.

____

____

____

God's Workmanship

> Thank you for making me so wonderfully complex! Your workmanship is marvelous—how well I know it. (Ps. 139:14 NLT)

> For we are his workmanship, created in Christ Jesus for good works, which God prepared beforehand, that we should walk in them. (Eph. 2:10 ESV)

You've been created by the perfect Creator. Don't complain about his workmanship.

____

____

____

JUSTIFIED

> Yet God, in his grace, freely makes us right in his sight. He did this through Christ Jesus when he freed us from the penalty for our sins. (Rom. 3:24 NLT)

> But you were washed, but you were sanctified, but you were justified in the name of the Lord Jesus and by the Spirit of our God. (1 Cor. 6:11 NKJV)

Tidbits & Morsels: You were made right with Christ—not by anything you did, but by what Jesus did.

____

____

____

LOVED BY GOD

> For God so loved the world that He gave His only begotten Son, that whoever believes in Him should not perish but have everlasting life. (John 3:16 NKJV)

> I have been crucified with Christ; it is no longer I who live, but Christ lives in me; and the life which I now live

> in the flesh I live by faith in the Son of God, who loved me and gave Himself for me. (Gal. 2:20 NKJV)

> We know, dear brothers and sisters, that God loves you and has chosen you to be his own people. (1 Thess. 1:4 NLT)

Tidbits & Morsels: God can't stop loving you ... because he doesn't want to.

___

___

___

New Creation

> Could it be any clearer? Our old way of life was nailed to the cross with Christ, a decisive end to that sin-miserable life—no longer captive to sin's demands! (Rom. 6:6 MSG)

> I have been crucified with Christ; it is no longer I who live, but Christ lives in me; and the life which I now live in the flesh I live by faith in the Son of God, who loved me and gave Himself for me. (Gal. 2:20 NKJV)

Tidbits & Morsels: Jesus died to give you a new life. Sometimes, when the road gets hard, you think about going back to your old life. Don't. Truth is, you won't fit in anymore.

___

___

___

No Longer Condemned

> So there is now no condemnation awaiting those who belong to Christ Jesus. (Rom. 8:1 TLB)

> Yet when we are judged by the Lord, we are being disciplined so that we will not be condemned along with the world. (1 Cor. 11:32 NLT)

Tidbits & Morsels: Jesus paid the price! You are innocent and free! Stop talkin' trash about yourself.

____

____

____

One in the Spirit with the Lord

> But the person who is joined to the Lord is one spirit with him. (1 Cor. 6:17 NLT)

> Each of us is a part of the one body of Christ. Some of us are Jews, some are Gentiles, some are slaves, and some are free. But the Holy Spirit has fitted us all together into one body. We have been baptized into Christ's body by the one Spirit, and have all been given that same Holy Spirit. (1 Cor. 12:13 TLB)

Tidbits & Morsels: If you're truly one with the Spirit, what does your shadow reflect?

____

____

____

One with Those in Christ

> There is neither Jew nor Gentile, neither slave nor free, nor is there male and female, for you are all one in Christ Jesus. (Gal. 3:28 NIV)

> This is how we've come to understand and experience love: Christ sacrificed his life for us. This is why we ought to live sacrificially for our fellow believers, and not just be out for ourselves. (1 John 3:16 MSG)

Tidbits & Morsels: As a believer in Christ, you have siblings around the world—play nice!—and many more waiting for you in heaven.

____

____

____

Righteousness of Christ

> God made him who had no sin to be sin for us, so that in him we might become the righteousness of God. (2 Cor. 5:21 NIV)

> But whatever were gains to me I now consider loss for the sake of Christ. What is more, I consider everything a loss because of the surpassing worth of knowing Christ Jesus my Lord, for whose sake I have lost all things. I consider them garbage, that I may gain Christ and be found in him, not having a righteousness of my own that comes from the law, but that which is through faith in Christ—the righteousness that comes from God on the basis of faith. (Phil. 3:7–9 NIV)

Tidbits & Morsels: When Jesus paid your sin debt, he assigned (imputed) his righteousness to you.

____

____

____

Saint

To the church of God that is in Corinth, to those sanctified in Christ Jesus, called to be saints together with all those who in every place call upon the name of our Lord Jesus Christ, both their Lord and ours. (1 Cor. 1:2 ESV)

Now you are no longer strangers to God and foreigners to heaven, but you are members of God's very own family, citizens of God's country, and you belong in God's household with every other Christian. What a foundation you stand on now: the apostles and the prophets; and the cornerstone of the building is Jesus Christ himself! We who believe are carefully joined together with Christ as parts of a beautiful, constantly growing temple for God. (Eph. 2:19–21 TLB)

Tidbits & Morsels: Don't get too full of yourself. You are only considered a saint because of your relationship with Christ.

____

____

____

Seated with Christ in the Heavenlies

[Jesus] When he finally arrives, blazing in beauty and all his angels with him, the Son of Man will take his place on his glorious throne. Then all the nations will be arranged before him and he will sort the people out, much as a shepherd sorts out sheep and goats, putting sheep to his right and goats to his left. Then the King will say to those on his right, "Enter, you who are blessed by my Father! Take what's coming to you in this kingdom. It's been ready for you since the world's foundation." (Matt. 25:31–34 MSG)

For he raised us from the dead along with Christ and seated us with him in the heavenly realms because we are united with Christ Jesus. (Eph. 2:6 NLT)

Tidbits & Morsels: No matter which verb tense is used, you have a seat in heaven with Christ. Period.

Set Free in Christ

> [Jesus] The Spirit of the Lord is on me, because he has anointed me to proclaim good news to the poor. He has sent me to proclaim freedom for the prisoners and recovery of sight for the blind, to set the oppressed free, to proclaim the year of the Lord's favor. (Luke 4:18–19 NIV)

> For the power of the life-giving Spirit—and this power is mine through Christ Jesus—has freed me from the vicious circle of sin and death. (Rom. 8:2 TLB)

Tidbits & Morsels: You don't have to follow a legalistic eating plan to lose weight. You are free to make your own choices in Christ.

Temple of the Holy Spirit

> Do you not know that you are God's temple and that God's Spirit dwells in you? If anyone destroys God's temple, God will destroy him. For God's temple is holy, and you are that temple. (1 Cor. 3:16–17 ESV)

> Don't you realize that all of you together are the house of God, and that the Spirit of God lives among you in his

> house? If anyone defiles and spoils God's home, God will destroy him. For God's home is holy and clean, and you are that home. (1 Cor. 6:19–20 TLB)

Tidbits & Morsels: When you belong to God, your body is his temple—not your dumpster.

____

____

____

APPENDIX I: BOOKS OF THE BIBLE & ABBREVIATIONS

Old Testament (ESV format)

Genesis (Gen.)
Exodus (Ex.)
Leviticus (Lev.)
Numbers (Num.)
Deuteronomy (Deut.)
Joshua (Josh.)
Judges (Judg.)
Ruth (Ruth)
1 Samuel (1 Sam.)
2 Samuel (2 Sam.)
1 Kings (1 Kings)
2 Kings (2 Kings)
1 Chronicles (1 Chron.)
2 Chronicles (2 Chron.)
Ezra (Ezra)
Nehemiah (Neh.)
Esther (Est.)
Job (Job)
Psalms (Ps.)
Proverbs (Prov.)
Ecclesiastes (Eccl.)
Song of Solomon (Song)
Isaiah (Isa.)
Jeremiah (Jer.)
Lamentations (Lam.)
Ezekiel (Ezek.)
Daniel (Dan.)
Hosea (Hos.)
Joel (Joel)
Amos (Amos)
Obadiah (Obad.)
Jonah (Jonah)
Micah (Mic.)
Nahum (Nah.)
Habakkuk (Hab.)
Zephaniah (Zeph.)
Haggai (Hag.)
Zechariah (Zech.)
Malachi (Mal.)

New Testament

Matthew (Matt.)
Mark (Mark)
Luke (Luke)
John (John)
Acts (Acts
Romans (Rom.)
1 Corinthians (1 Cor.)
2 Corinthians (2 Cor.)
Galatians (Gal.)
Ephesians (Eph.)
Philippians (Phil.)
Colossians (Col.)
1 Thessalonians (1 Thess.)
2 Thessalonians (2 Thess.)
1 Timothy (1 Tim.)
2 Timothy (2 Tim.)
Titus (Titus)
Philemon (Philem.)
Hebrews (Heb.)
James (James)
1 Peter (1 Pet.)
2 Peter (2 Pet.)
1 John (1 John)
2 John (2 John)
3 John (3 John)
Jude (Jude)
Revelation (Rev.)

APPENDIX II: A PERSONAL RELATIONSHIP WITH JESUS

If you would like to have a personal relationship with Jesus, start by reading the following verses from Romans (NLT), the Apostle Paul's letter to the church in Rome:

1. No one is righteous—not even one. No one is truly wise; no one is seeking God. All have turned away; all have become useless. No one does good, not a single one. (3:10–12)
2. For the wages of sin is death, but the free gift of God is eternal life through Christ Jesus our Lord. (6:23)
3. But God showed his great love for us by sending Christ to die for us while we were still sinners. (5:8)
4. For "Everyone who calls on the name of the LORD will be saved." (10:13)
5. Therefore, since we have been made right in God's sight by faith, we have peace with God because of what Jesus Christ our Lord has done for us. (5:1)
6. So now there is no condemnation for those who belong to Christ Jesus. (8:1)
7. And I am convinced that nothing can ever separate us from God's love. Neither death nor life, neither angels nor demons, neither our fears for today nor our worries about tomorrow—not even the powers

> of hell can separate us from God's love. No power in the sky above or in the earth below—indeed, nothing in all creation will ever be able to separate us from the love of God that is revealed in Christ Jesus our Lord. (8:38–39)

To accept Jesus Christ as your Lord and Savior, pray the prayer below from your heart:

> Dear Lord,
>
> In my heart and in my soul, I sincerely want to have a true and personal relationship with you, Jesus. Therefore, as the Bible instructs me, I answer your call to follow you.
>
> I believe you died on the cross for my sins, and I confess I am a sinner and ask for your forgiveness. Please, I invite you to come into my life as my Lord and my Savior. Help me serve and obey you and become the person you want me to be.
>
> Thank you, Lord, for hearing and answering my prayer, for forgiving me, and for giving me the gift of eternal life. Amen.

If you prayed this prayer, tell someone. Romans 10:9 says, "If you confess with your mouth that Jesus is Lord and believe in your heart that God raised him from the dead, you will be saved."

As the Apostle Paul prayed for the church in Ephesus (3:16–19 NIV), I offer this prayer for you:

> I pray that out of his glorious riches he may strengthen you with power through his Spirit in your inner being, so that Christ may dwell in your hearts through faith. And I pray that you, being rooted and established in love, may have power, together with all the Lord's holy people, to grasp how wide and long and high and

> deep is the love of Christ, and to know this love that surpasses knowledge—that you may be filled to the measure of all the fullness of God.

As with any personal relationship, you need to spend time with Jesus to get to know him on a deeper level. Here are some ways you can do that:

- Read, study, and meditate on the Word of God daily.
- Apply what you learn to your behavior.
- Pray in Jesus's name.
- Talk to God as you would with anyone with whom you want a close relationship.
- Listen for the voice of his Holy Spirit and obey his commands.
- Confess your sins to God.
- Forgive others as God forgives you.
- Thank God each day for your blessings.
- Praise and worship the Lord God Almighty.
- Meet on a regular basis with like-minded Christians.

If you'd like to speak with someone about your decision, here are some prayer lines for you to consider:

- 1-800-700-7000: 700 Club
- 1-888-388-2683: Billy Graham Evangelistic Association and Franklin Graham Ministries
- 1-800-525-5683: K-Love Christian Music Radio Programming Service
- 1-800-947-5433: Life Outreach International
- 1-714-731-1000: TBN Prayer Line

Also, to learn more about God and what he thinks of you, see PART III: THE GOD YOU SERVE and PART IV: WHAT GOD SAYS ABOUT YOU.

APPENDIX III: OBJECTIONS OVERCOME

(This condensed list was put together by Heidi Bylsma -Epperson of www.thinwithin.org and used with her permission.)

OBJECTION 1: There is too much freedom in this approach. I need someone to tell me what to eat and when I'm going to get to (and maintain) a healthy size.

RESPONSE 1: Jesus came down from heaven and took on the limitations of a human body—in effect, setting much of His freedom aside, so that we could be free from the hold of anything that would keep us from the life He intends for us. He never intended for food to torment us. He intended only that it bless us.

In Thin Within, we learn that freedom means freedom not just to eat whatever tasty morsel we want when hungry. It means freedom NOT to have to eat a certain food but being able (and willing) to say no! What this inspires is a deep dependence on God to strengthen us by the power of His Spirit inside of us. This impacts not just our food and eating and our bodies, but it affects us emotionally, physically, and spiritually, too.

> It is for freedom that Christ has set us free. Stand firm, then, and do not let yourselves be burdened again by

> a yoke of slavery. (Gal. 5:1 NIV)

Objection 2: I have tried this before and it doesn't work.

Response 2: Typically, when a participant has said "... it doesn't work," they mean Thin Within hasn't worked for weight loss as fast as they want. And, to be honest with you, it means that they may or may not have been honest with themselves about eating less food.

But we want to think God's thoughts about the goal, don't we? He doesn't want us thin nearly so much as He wants us *His*. And while we don't have to pick between the two, often we sell ourselves just to get thin, even while the diet we use shreds our souls.

What if God's goal is something else first? What if you have gotten on the scale after being so confident that you have eaten so much less food and you are sorely disappointed to see the numbers not only not going down but actually up a smidge? Could God be placing a divine toe on the scale so that your gaze, rather than being on the man-made scale, you look at Him, instead? Does the "idol of thin" have its claws in your heart? For many of us, it does.

That, too, is a stronghold. Our God will not share our hearts with any other.

> I press on toward the goal to win the prize for which God has called me heavenward in Christ Jesus. (Phil. 3:14 NIV)

Objection 3: I was a part of a similar program and felt condemned all the time. I just can't "go there" again!

Response 3: Many of our participants haven't heard that Thin Within began in 1975. They began their own Christian mindful eating journey with another program (that didn't start until 1986), a program that encourages eating between hunger and "full." Many of these participants had great success, too.

Then, heartache came as the teaching they loved diverged from the pure Truth of the Scriptures. The motivation offered by the leadership was condemning at best and possibly dangerous.

Thin Within reminds us: We can never hate ourselves into positive change.

> If we claim to be without sin, we deceive ourselves, and the truth is not in us. If we confess our sins, he is faithful and just and will forgive us our sins and purify us from all unrighteousness. (1 John 1:8–9 NIV)

OBJECTION 4: I fail all the time.

RESPONSE 4: Yep, we do, too. All of us in Thin Within. It is, in fact, the human condition! Perfectionism is a lie rooted in pride! OUCH! Since we WILL fail, we might as well have a plan for failure. We have found that the best approach is the one that invites God in. Again. And again. And again. In fact, this is a game changer! When we invite Him IN to our failures, we can learn things like "What was going on that caused me to slip?" and "What can I do differently to be on your page the next time, Lord?"

This is true observation and correction. What many people call observation and correction is really our own opinion looking at our mess-up and wagging our own finger in our face and saying "Just stop it! Eat less next time!" If Jesus had just five minutes to speak in person with you, about the most important thing on his heart, I don't think he would say to you, "Now then, Emily, about your eating." Or, "About your weight." He is loving.

> Let us then approach God's throne of grace with confidence, so that we may receive mercy and find grace

> to help us in our time of need. (Heb. 4:16 NIV)

Objection 5: Our bodies, because of sin, are no longer perfect as in the garden of Eden. How do we know we can truly rely on our sinful bodies to tell us the truth of when we are full and hungry? Is it because we are new creatures in Christ? I know we are spiritually, but we still have the same fallen bodies.

Response 5: You are exactly right. We DO have spiritually fallen bodies. They aren't perfect. But thankfully, we have the Holy Spirit of God at work in us and not only that, but the fundamental signals that God gave us for all kinds of things, are reliable. Including hunger and satisfied, as we lean into the Holy Spirit to show us!

My body, though fallen, tells me reliably when I need to go to the bathroom, when I need more rest, when I have my hand on something too hot, or when I am sick. I don't question the reliability of these signals due to the fall of my flesh! If I did, there might be some consequences!

The problem with my hunger/satisfied signals isn't so much in the physical aspect of my fallen body. It is in the deceitfulness of my heart! Time and time again, we justify eating outside of our 0 to 5 boundaries. We act entitled to eat when we have had a hard day, when we celebrate, etc.!

> Test me, Lord, and try me, examine my heart and my mind. (Ps. 26:2 NIV)

Objection 6: I'm concerned about eating as little as Thin Within recommends. I'm a breast cancer survivor and wondered if there's research on the body still getting what it needs nutrition-wise. I realize most food doesn't even truly feed our bodies these days.

Response 6: Thin Within encourages each person to invite the Lord to help them to know what their body needs.

Typically, God will show us through the signals that He has placed in our bodies—hunger and satisfaction. If your body needs more fuel, you will know it by the signal of hunger.

Since the foods we often eat are not as nutrition-dense as we might think or hope due to many modern practices in food manufacturing, we encourage all to consider the use of supplements by consulting with their medical practitioner.

Objection 7: When I tried Thin Within, I felt overwhelmed, very much a failure and a condemned sinner, for overeating. I think I struggle with the idea that taking one or two bites past a 5 (satisfied) is willful sin, not to mention that I may not be convinced where or what my signal for "satisfied" is.

Response 7: I am so sorry for the condemnation you have felt! It is our desire to speak the message of grace again and again in Thin Within. John 3:17 says that God sent Jesus into the world not to condemn the world, but that the world might be saved through Him. Another passage is similar: Romans 8:1 (ESV) says, "Therefore there is now no condemnation for those who are in Christ. Jesus."

Far from condemning, our God is restorative.

> He who did not spare his own Son, but gave him up for us all—how will he not also, along with him, graciously give us all things? (Rom. 8:32 NIV)

Our God loves to be invited into the mess-up so He can equip us for victory going forward. It is His kindness that leads us to repentance (Rom. 2:4). His view of failure is vastly different from our own. Perfectionism is a lie. If He doesn't condemn us, why should we condemn ourselves? We can't hate ourselves into a positive change!

Thin Within does not teach that one bite or two past 5 is a sin. In fact, it isn't about food at all. It is about our hearts. God doesn't want us thin as much as He wants us HIS. He wants our hearts.

Objection 8: I can't subscribe to the Thin Within approach because you don't value physical exercise. Since my body is God's temple, I know that, to honor Him, I need to exercise.

Response 8: First, a correction: We LOVE exercise! We encourage people to apply the 0 to 5 principle we teach for our eating (moderation) to exercise and activity. Moderation is good in all things! If my body needs activity, I move it. And kind of like with the foods that I select when I need fuel, I use discernment to select activities I enjoy and that work for my body when I need movement. Once I have had enough, or am at a "5" activity wise, I stop. Far from teaching against exercise and activity, we absolutely think it is vital to a person's emotional, physical, and spiritual health!

Objection 9: You guys teach that this is the only way to manage weight. I don't agree with that. I don't think it is sinful to diet or less spiritual to diet.

Response 9: Thin Within does not assert that a person is ungodly, sinning, or even less spiritual if they choose another means for managing their relationship with food. God leads each of us uniquely. The last thing we want to do is provide yet another topic to divide the Church of God!

Thin Within ministers to those who want out of dieting for any reason. They often have struggled with self-loathing and condemnation, performance, and a constant sense of failure. They, like me, may be a "weaker sister" when it comes to dieting. They just aren't sure how to do it without the diet and "thin" being idols. They can't diet in freedom. We are well aware that this doesn't describe everyone, but it may describe 90% of the people who come to Thin Within—or more!

Objection 10: I work with only a very quick minute for breaks to eat. I end up eating in a hurry so I end up eating too much in an effort to be sure I won't get hungry before the next time I can eat. Eating in a relaxed environment isn't likely to happen.

RESPONSE 10: As with other objections on this journey, we encourage you to invite the Lord in and ask Him to give you the help you need to know how to approach this challenge. He cares. You can experiment a bit—at first, on your days off—with various foods to see which pack a powerful kick in terms of sustaining you. For many of us that might come in the form of jerky, nutrition bars (with protein and healthy fats), yogurt, hard boiled eggs, or cheese, and the like. The goal will be to experience satisfaction with just a few peaceful bites.

If there is any way you can have nuts for a quick pick-me-up if you get to a 0 when you can't eat yet (or something else accessible even as you head to the restroom), this can help a lot as well.

For the complete, unedited list of objections, go to this link: https://www.thinwithinacademy.com/AnswersToObjections

APPENDIX IV: ACKNOWLEDGMENTS

Over the last forty years, I have become more and more thankful to the Lord for teaching me how to *apply* Scripture in all areas of my life. In *Say Grace: A Scriptural Field Guide to Weight Loss*, the application dealt with my relationship with food. While I worked on this manuscript, God's Word nourished me spiritually, emotionally, intellectually, and physically. And by his grace, for his glory, I released my extra weight.

I'd like to acknowledge the team of advanced readers who reviewed this compilation and offered valuable input, encouragement, and support:

Judy Wardell Halliday, founder of Thin Within Ministries and author of *Thin Within* and *Hunger Within*, who wrote the foreword to this field guide.

Heidi Bylsma-Epperson, owner and coach at ThinWithin.org, who gave me full access to her online material and also wrote an endorsement.

Rev. Dr. Paul R. Berube, Senior Pastor at Gate City Church (Nashua, NH) for his time and personal endorsement.

Fellow authors Kathleen D. Bailey, Linda B. Davis, Andy Davison, Cynthia Fantasia, Janet Grunst, Lori Roeleveld, and Terrie Todd for their enthusiastic endorsements.

Friends Debra Bock, Darlene Gibson, Joyce Goldthwaite, Andrea Hamilton, and Kim Parker for their kind words and intuitive suggestions.

Though my husband David passed away on August 18, 2021, I want to honor his memory by giving him due credit. He was the best sounding board ever! We talked over every topic and walked through the Scriptures hand-in-hand. He cheered me on in my weight loss journey, too, even during his final weeks in the hospital. I am so grateful for the fifteen years we had together.

Once again, I thank the team at Elk Lake Publishing, Inc. for their patience and professionalism: publisher Deb Haggerty; editors Paul Conant and Judy Hagey; and format and cover designer Derinda Babcock. You have blessed me over and over!

APPENDIX V: ABOUT THE AUTHOR

Clarice G. James

Smart, Fun, & Relatable

Twenty plus years ago, Clarice G. James compiled a series of seven topical booklets titled *The Word Applied* with subtitles of *God, Salvation, Hope & Healing, Emotions, Family, Workplace,* and *Grief. Say Grace: A Scriptural Field Guide to Weight Loss* is her first full-length topical compilation.

Clarice has also authored five contemporary women's novels: *Party of One*, *Doubleheader*, *Manhattan Grace*, *The Girl He Knew,* and *The Least of These.* Her stories are woven together with colorful threads of humor, faith, romance, and mystery.

When she isn't writing, Clarice loves to host author events, conduct writing workshops, or speak to women's groups on the spiritual themes in her novels. She also enjoys home decorating projects, books clubs, and Bible studies.

Clarice currently lives in southern New Hampshire. Though widowed in 1998, then again in 2021, she is comforted by an abundance of sweet memories and blessed by her attentive children and fun grandchildren.

You can order any of Clarice's books at your local bookstore or online at Amazon.

Party of One

Doubleheader

Manhattan Grace

The Girl He Knew

The Least of These

APPENDIX VI: REFERENCES & RESOURCES

- BibleGateway.com, HarperCollins Publishers, 10 East 53rd Street, New York NY 10022
- English Standard Version ESV® Text Edition: 2016. © 2001, Crossway Bibles, a publishing ministry of Good News Publishers. Since the ESV is the primary resource used in this compilation, all abbreviations follow the ESV's format.
- The Living Bible © 1971 by Tyndale House Foundation. Used by permission of Tyndale House Publishers Inc., Carol Stream, Illinois 60188. All rights reserved.
- The Message © 1993, 2002, 2018 by Eugene H. Peterson
- New International Version ®, NIV® Copyright ©1973, 1978, 1984, 2011 by Biblica, Inc.® Used by permission. All rights reserved worldwide.
- New King James Version ®, Copyright © 1982 by Thomas Nelson. Used by permission. All rights reserved.
- New Living Translation © 1996, 2004, 2015 by Tyndale House Foundation. Used by permission of Tyndale House Publishers, Inc., Carol Stream, Illinois 60188. All rights reserved.

- "Objections Overcome," Heidi Bylsma-Epperson, www.thinwithin.org
- Rebuilding God's Temple—Discovering God's Master Plan, ThinWithin.org, 2003
- Thin Within, Judy Halliday, R.N. and Arthur Halliday, M.D., Thomas Nelson, 2002

APPENDIX VI: PROGRESS REPORT

Date	Weight	Date	Weight

Date:	Weight	Date	Weight

Date:	Weight	Date	Weight

Date:	Weight	Date	Weight

Date:	Weight	Date	Weight

Date:	Weight	Date	Weight

Made in the USA
Middletown, DE
02 October 2022